real life
intermediate

WORKBOOK

contents

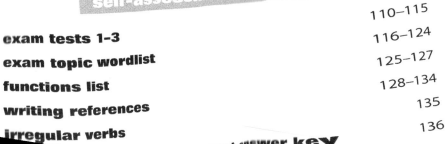
...nt and exam test answer key

*   easy to do
**   a bit harder
*** extra challenge

Vocabulary

Education

1 Match the adjectives 1–3 with the opposites a–c. Which of them can be followed by the noun *school*? Which can be followed by *subject*?

1 private
2 compulsory
3 mixed

a single-sex
b state
c optional

_____ school   _____ subject

2 Complete the text with the words from the box.

> compulsory   discipline   head teacher
> main   mixed   optional   private ✓
> pupils   rules   single-sex   specialises
> staff   state   uniforms

✕

Is your school special? Tell us about it.

I went to a ¹ _private_ school before, but it was too expensive. Then we found Cutherstone Sports College. It's a ² _____ school, but it's quite unusual. It ³ _____ in sports. The ⁴ _____ subjects include Maths, English, a foreign language, PE and two additional sports: those are the things everyone has to do. I want to become a dancer, so my ⁵ _____ subjects are gymnastics and dance, but I also do a few other sports as ⁶ _____ subjects.

There are eight PE teachers in the school, and one of them is the ⁷ _____ _____. The ⁸ _____ are friendly and support us when we have important competitions. Is there a lot of ⁹ _____ ? It depends. We don't wear ¹⁰ _____ ; a lot of the time we walk around in sports clothes anyway. But there are safety ¹¹ _____ – they are necessary when such a lot of people are doing sports.

Many years ago, Cutherstone was a ¹² _____ school, for boys only. At that time, some people believed that sport was not so important for girls. But now it's a ¹³ _____ school; exactly half of the ¹⁴ _____ are girls, and last year the girls' football team won the local championship.

Grammar

Present simple and continuous

3 ⟨*⟩ Underline the correct form to complete the sentences.

1 This term we *read/are reading* Macbeth.
2 My little sister *goes/is going* to school for the first time next month.
3 Sam *finishes/is finishing* school at 15.30 every day except Friday.
4 Online courses *become/are becoming* more popular these days.
5 In democratic schools students *vote/are voting* on the rules.
6 I can't go out right now. I *work/am working* on my Geography project.

4 ⟨**⟩ Put the words in the correct order to make sentences.

1 sometimes/homework/help/her/sister/I/my/with.
I _sometimes help my sister with her homework._
2 twice/play/week/We/a/basketball
We _____.
3 school/cycle/usually/doesn't/to/Tim
Tim _____.
4 you/Do/meet/school/after/always
Do _____?
5 Ric/month/to/flying/Deb/and/are/next/India.
Deb _____.

Grammar plus: Time expressions

5 ⟨***⟩ Put the time expressions and adverbs of frequency in the correct position in each sentence. Sometimes more than one position is possible.

1 I don't play tennis after dinner. (often)
I don't often play tennis after dinner.
2 The whole class goes on a school trip. (three times a year)

_____.
3 We have really interesting discussions in class. (some days)

_____.
4 Pete forgets about birthdays. (seldom)

_____.
5

6 (✱✱) Complete the email with the verbs in brackets in the correct present tense.

❌

To: alexb78@gmail.com
From: jb1990@hotmail.com
Subject: School in Korea

Hi Alex,

You wanted me to tell you about my school here in Korea. Well, we ¹ _work_ (work) really hard. School ² _____ (start) at 8.30 a.m. and ³ _____ (finish) at 7 p.m. There's a lunch break at 1.30 p.m. and we ⁴ _____ (have) lunch in our classrooms. In lessons we ⁵ _____ (listen) to the teacher and ⁶ _____ (answer) questions. We ⁷ _____ (not/give) our opinions and we ⁸ _____ (not/have) discussions.

We ⁹ _____ (take) final exams next month, so right now we ¹⁰ _____ (prepare) for them really intensively. Every day after school I ¹¹ _____ (go) to an evening school called an 'academy' for extra lessons. I ¹² _____ (return) home after 10 p.m. and then I ¹³ _____ (do) my homework. It's really hard, but my results ¹⁴ _____ (improve).

I hope you ¹⁵ _____ (not/work) so much these days. Write when you have a moment.

Best wishes,

Jeong Bin

7 (✱✱✱) Complete the questions 1–5 with the correct form of the verbs in brackets. Then match them to the answers a–e.

1 How often _do you do_ (you/do) sports?
2 _____ (you/read) anything interesting at the moment?
3 _____ (you/have) any special responsibilities at school?
4 _____ (you/take) any exams this year?
5 How often _____ (your English teacher/ set) homework?

a In every lesson.
b I play tennis twice a week and go swimming every Friday.
c No, next year.
d Yes, a book about cycling around the world.
e Yes, I do. I clean the classroom once a month.

8 (✱✱✱) Give answers that are true for you to the questions in exercise 7.

1 _____ .
2 _____ .
3 _____ .
4 _____ .
5 _____ .

Grammar reference

Present simple and present continuous

Use of the present simple

- We use the present simple to talk about actions or events that happen repeatedly (routines, habits):

*Robert **goes** to the gym every Sunday.*

- We use the present simple to talk about things that are always true (general truths):

*Most insects **eat** plants and other insects.*

Time expressions with the present simple

- *every day/week/month/year/afternoon/Tuesday*, etc. These usually go at the end of the sentence:

*We **play** basketball **every Wednesday**.*

- *once/twice/three times a day/week/month/year*, etc. These usually go at the end of the sentence:

*I **visit** my grandparents **twice a month**.*

- *some/most days/weeks/months*, etc. These usually go at the beginning of the sentence:

*Some days I **feel** very isolated and lonely.*

- Adverbs of frequency. These usually go just before the main verb:

*I **usually have** cereal for breakfast.*
*They **don't often go** on holiday abroad.*
*Does she **always cycle** to school?*

100% ▓▓▓▓▓▓▓▓▓▓▓▓▓▓▓▓▓▓▓▓▓▓▓▓▓▓▓▓▓▓▓▓ 0%

| always | usually/ normally | often | sometimes | not often | rarely/ seldom | never |

Use of the present continuous

- We use the present continuous to talk about things that are happening now (at the time of speaking):

*He's **talking** on the phone now.*

- We use the present continuous to talk about things that are happening around the time when we speak (not necessarily at the moment of speaking):

*In History this term, we're **studying** the Romans.*

- We use the present continuous to express current changes:

*My school grades **are getting** better this year.*

- We can also use the present continuous to talk about a definite future arrangement:

*We're **flying** to Barcelona next Thursday.*

Time expressions with the present continuous

- For things happening now, we use:

at the moment, (right) now, today, this morning/afternoon, this week/month/year, these days, at present

- To talk about future arrangements, we use:

tomorrow, next week/month/Monday, on Tuesday/Saturday

Vocabulary

Education and work

1 Match the sentence beginnings 1–7 with the endings a–g.

1 Kate's doing
2 You're going to fail
3 I'm going to university
4 Emily's just started
5 Zoe earns
6 Richard passed
7 I've applied

a a higher salary than her husband.
b all his exams with very good marks.
c for a job with a small company.
d secondary school this year.
e to get a degree in computing.
f well in her coursework this year.
g your Science exam if you don't revise.

2 Complete the sentences with the words from the box.

degree career job ✓ pay salary sack

1 Jessica is going to apply for a _job_ in Thailand.
2 They promised me a _____ rise after two years.
3 My ambition is to have a successful _____ in the media.
4 Alan got the _____ from his job for being late just once!
5 My granddad went to university when he was seventeen and got a _____ when he was nineteen.
6 Ryan earns a good _____ in his new job.

3 Complete the sentences with nouns, adjectives or verbs formed from the words in brackets.

1 Jack's grandma had a _successful_ (success) career as a doctor.
2 He hasn't got the right _____ (qualify) for this job.
3 After a year of hard work, Sue got _____ (promote) and a pay rise.
4 Sophie's doing an _____ (apprentice) with a large company.
5 Job _____ (satisfy) is more important to me than a high salary.

Grammar

State and activity verbs

4 a (✱) Put the verbs from the box into the correct columns in the table.

act ✓ agree ✓ know learn love
remember see seem sound study
want wear

Activity verbs	State verbs		
	feeling	thought/ opinion	appearance the senses
act	agree		

b (✱✱) Complete the sentences with the correct tense (present simple or present continuous) of the state and activity verbs from exercise 4a.

1 Little Billy _doesn't want_ (not/want) to go to school.
2 We _____ (study) hard for our exams these days.
3 _____ (you/see) that cloud? It's a funny shape.
4 I _____ (act) in the school musical next month.
5 Your idea _____ (sound) really good.
6 We all _____ (agree) that it's a good plan.
7 I _____ (learn) to play the piano now.
8 I _____ (love) art lessons.
9 Millie _____ (wear) a lovely dress today.
10 The children _____ (seem) quite happy here.
11 I _____ (not/remember) where I've put my keys.
12 _____ (you/know) this word?

5 (✱✱) Underline the correct verb form.

1 Mum *cooks/is cooking* something. It *smells/is smelling* delicious.
2 We *don't need/aren't needing* a new car. The old one *is/is being* still okay.
3 Which optional course *do you prefer/are you preferring*? I *take/am taking* drama this year.
4 *Do you hear/Are you hearing* that sound? I think someone *plays/is playing* the violin.
5 Jack *hates/is hating* his school uniform. Right now he *wears/is wearing* the trousers and shirt, but not the jacket.
6 'Why *is Amy crying/does Amy cry*?' 'She *doesn't understand/isn't understanding* her Maths homework.'

6 (✱✱) Complete the sentences with the correct tense (present simple or present continuous) of the verbs in brackets.

1 'What film *are you watching* (you/watch)?' 'The Godfather. I really *like* (like) it.'
2 Tom _____ (behave) a bit strangely. He _____ (seem) worried.
3 I _____ (not believe) that man. He _____ (not tell) us the truth.
4 Daniel _____ (not care) about his exam results. Everyone _____ (revise) but he _____ (do) nothing!
5 This coffee _____ (taste) wonderful. _____ (you/make) some more?
6 I _____ (not mind) coursework. I _____ (work) on a project now and I quite _____ (like) it.

7 (✱✱✱) Decide if the verb in brackets in each sentence describes an activity or a state. Complete the sentences with the correct verb form in brackets.

1 I *don't think* (not/think) you should go there.
2 I can't concentrate. I _____ (think) about the holidays.
3 My parents _____ (think) I'm not studying hard enough.
4 'Mike _____ (have) breakfast.' 'But it's one p.m.!'
5 I _____ (have) a new guitar.
6 Laura _____ (have) a degree in mathematics.
7 You can talk to him now, he _____ (have) a break.
8 The new computer lab _____ (look) great.
9 We _____ (just/look) at these dresses.

Grammar reference

State and activity verbs

Activity (dynamic) verbs describe activities. We use them in the present simple or the present continuous tense:

*Bethany often **watches** TV.* (a habit)
*She's **watching** a film now.* (at the moment of speaking)

State (stative) verbs describe states. We do not normally use them in the present continuous (they don't take *-ing* form), even if they refer to things or states happening at the moment of speaking:

*I **don't understand** her.*
*She **doesn't want** my help.*

Common state verbs

• *be, have, need*:

I'm very hungry.
*We **don't have** much time to spare.*
*How much money **do** you **need**?*

• *hate, like, love, prefer, care, don't mind, want* (verbs which describe emotions/feelings):

*Matthew **hates** getting up early on Sundays.*
*I **don't mind** which film we see.*

• *believe, know, remember, forget, agree, think, understand* (verbs which express thoughts/opinions):

*I **don't believe** in ghosts.*
*I **remember** that girl from school.*

• *feel, hear, see, taste, smell, sound, look, seem* (verbs which refer to the senses or appearance):

*This cake **tastes** delicious.*
*You **seem** pleased with yourself.*

Some state verbs can have an 'active' meaning, for example *think, have, look*. We use them in the present continuous tense like other activity verbs:

*I **think** Tom's very intelligent.* (*think* here means believe and refers to a state)

*What **are** you **thinking** about?* (*think* here means consider and refers to a mental activity)

*She **has** two brothers.* (*has* here means possesses and refers to a state)

*I'll call you later. We **are** just **having** dinner.* (*have* here means eat and refers to an activity)

*Your new haircut **looks** great!* (*look* here means appearance and refers to a state)

*I'm **looking** for my mobile phone.* (*look* here means search and refers to an activity)

Vocabulary

Improve your concentration

1 Match the verbs 1–7 with the nouns a–g.

1	make	a	distractions
2	solve	b	a decision
3	ignore	c	one's concentration
4	improve	d	important skills
5	set	e	sense (of something)
6	learn	f	problems
7	make	g	goals

2 Complete the sentences using the correct form of the expressions from exercise 1.

1 When I have to _make a decision_ , I think about things before deciding what to do.

2 I like to _____ myself _____ – I think it's important to know what you want to achieve.

3 I don't understand this text at all, I just can't _____ of it.

4 When I revise for my exams I find it hard to _____ such as text messages from friends.

5 If you have a logical brain, then you probably find it easy to _____ .

6 I find it hard to pay attention in class. I need to _____ my _____ .

7 I'm doing business studies because I think the course helps you to _____ .

3 Complete the sentences with the noun or verb form of the word in brackets.

1 We have to write a _description_ (describe) of a friend for English homework.

2 You can find _____ (inform) about millions of different topics on the internet.

3 I studied really hard last year and paid _____ (attend) in class. There was a big _____ (improve) in my marks.

4 I find it hard to _____ (concentration) when I study, so I try not to have any _____ (distract) like music.

5 Jamie can _____ (persuasion) anyone to do anything, and he can _____ (organisation) anything!

6 That's a really difficult problem, I don't know what the _____ (solve) is.

Listening

4 **a** ② Listen to the radio programme about learning styles. Complete the descriptions with the correct learning styles below.

> concrete thinkers   abstract thinkers
> active processors   reflective processors

1 _____ make sense of an experience by thinking about it.

2 _____ learn by doing things.

3 _____ learn by observing and analysing things.

4 _____ make sense of an experience by quickly using the new information.

b Which is your learning style?

5 ② Listen again and choose the correct answers.

1 Tina thinks instruction books are
   a easy to use and understand.
   b boring but useful.
   c not worth reading.

2 Alex read his instruction book because
   a he wanted to find out how to store phone numbers on his computer.
   b he thinks you learn more if you read the instruction book.
   c he doesn't like experimenting with things, he prefers to follow instructions.

3 Vicky
   a usually enjoys reading instruction books *and* experimenting.
   b doesn't like people telling her what to do.
   c has a friend who taught her how to use her mobile.

4 Most people use
   a one main learning style.
   b at least three learning styles.
   c all four learning styles.

5 The presenter
   a is an active processor.
   b likes thinking about new experiences.
   c doesn't like learning new things.

6 Dr Jones thinks that
   a not everyone is clever because some people don't learn very well.
   b everyone is clever, but people are clever in different ways.
   c everyone is intelligent, but people should use a variety of learning styles.

Reading

6 Read the dictionary extracts, then look at the text title and pictures below. Answer the question, then read the text and check your answer.

The text is probably about

- **a** the most intelligent people in the world. ☐
- **b** how to develop your ability to think. ☐
- **c** why some people are good at games. ☐

brain power *n* your ability to think

challenge *v* to test someone's skills or abilities

expand *v* to make something bigger

strategic thinking thinking that is carefully planned in order to achieve something

stimulate *v* to encourage something to develop and improve

vary *v* to change something, to be different in different situations

routine *n* your usual way of doing things, especially when you do them in the same order at the same time every day

7 Read the text and match five of the headings below to the correct paragraph A–E. There is one extra heading.

1 Learn something new
2 Try puzzles and games
3 Vary your routine
4 Keep a diary or use a notebook
5 Stop playing computer games
6 Eat the right food

8 Read the text again and tick (✓) true or cross (✗) false.

1 ☐ You must do all five activities to develop your brain power.
2 ☐ Games like chess help to improve your ability to think and plan.
3 ☐ There are no computer games that can help develop your brain.
4 ☐ When you change your routine the brain gets better at making quick decisions.
5 ☐ Fish such as salmon are good for the brain because they contain omega-3.
6 ☐ People who learn lots of new skills always have a lot of friends.

Brain training

When you want to get fit, you go to the gym or do some exercise. But what about when you want to improve your concentration? Then you need to exercise your brain!

Here are our top five activities to improve the way your brain works and help you develop better focus and concentration – try one and see!

A ___

Do some crosswords or try sudoku. These types of puzzles stimulate the brain because you have to solve clues or use logic and reasoning to find the solutions. Practise your strategic thinking by playing games like chess, GO and Mancala – you'll find you can plan better in other areas of your life, too. If you love playing computer

games, then challenge yourself with one of the brain-training computer games. Once you try them, you won't want to stop!

B ___

We are creatures of habit and we often follow the same routine every day, so the brain becomes lazy. Try going to school by a different route one day a week, or using a different type of transport. Varying your routine challenges the brain and helps you to make quick decisions and solve problems.

C ___

Certain types of food can help your brain stay healthy and work well. Proteins are great for the brain so eat plenty of cheese, meat, fish and milk.

The brain also needs carbohydrates and some fat, and these come from fruit, vegetables, grains and olive oil. Omega-3 is a fantastic food for the brain, you find it in fish such as salmon and tuna. Remember, a balanced diet is essential for the brain.

D ___

Start a new hobby, learn a language, take up a new sport … it doesn't matter what you do. New activities stimulate the brain and expand the way the brain thinks. You can also learn important or useful skills and meet new friends.

E ___

Clever people write down their ideas. They organise their thoughts and set goals for things they want to do. Writing things down tells your brain it is producing good ideas, so it produces more ideas and better ideas. This is a great way to improve your brain power.

Writing

A formal letter of application

1 Write your address and the date in the top right corner.

2 Write the address of the person or organisation you are writing to on the left. Include the person's job title/department if you know it.

3 Begin the letter *Dear Sir/Madam* if you don't know the name of the person you are writing to. If you know the name, begin *Dear* + name. Use *Mr* for men, *Mrs* for married women and *Ms* for women when you don't know if they are married or not.

4 In **paragraph 1**, say why you are writing: *I am writing in connection with …* *I am writing about …* If appropriate, give dates. Say what you are enclosing with your letter, for example a photograph or a CV.

5 In **paragraph 2**, describe yourself and your background; give information about your age, your family and where you live.

6 In **paragraph 3**, describe your studies and interests.

7 In **paragraph 4**, describe your ambitions using phrases such as: *My dream is to …* *In the future I hop to …* Also give your reasons for apply *I would like to do course/study at th centre because it a good reputatio*

8 Say that you expect a reply: *I hope to hear fro you soon.* *I look forward to your reply.*

9 Close the letter v *Yours faithfully* if you began it wit *Dear Sir/Madam.* If you used *Dear* name, close the letter with *Yours sincerely.*

10 Sign the letter an then print your name or write it CAPITAL LETTER:

1085 Budapest
Krepesi út, 92
Magyarország
6 May 2010

The Head Teacher
Nottingham School
3 Stark Street
Nottingham
N2 8DD

Dear Mr Anderson,

I am writing to apply to study English at Nottingham School. I would like to study on the three-week summer course, starting on 4 July. I enclose my photograph.

My full name is Katalin Nagy. I am seventeen years old and I live with my parents in Budapest in Hungary.

I am currently studying for my school-leaving exams. I love learning languages and I also enjoy visiting other countries. Last year I stayed in France on an exchange programme. As a result, my French conversation skills have greatly improved. In addition, I enjoy meeting people from different cultures.

My ambition is to be a translator. I would like to study at Nottingham School because the course is recognised internationally and it has an excellent reputation.

I look forward to hearing from you.

Yours sincerely,

Katalin Nagy

Katalin Nagy

---

1 **Read the letter and answer the questions.**

1 Why is Katalin writing?

_____

2 Where does she live? Who does she live with?

_____

3 What are her interests?

_____

4 Why does she want to study at Nottingham School?

_____

2 **Read the sentences and look at the underlined words. Decide if the words indicate addition (A) or consequence (C). Then find and underline examples in the letter above.**

1 I would like to apply to participate in the music course and <u>also</u> live with an English family.   *A*

2 During the year I am always busy with school. <u>As a result</u>, I don't have enough time to practise.   ____

3 I love reading and watching films. <u>In addition</u>, I like doing sports.   ____

3 Complete the sentences with *also, in addition* or *as a result*.

1 I practise the piano a lot. _As a result_ , I play very well.

2 I like travelling. I _____ like meeting new people.

3 It will be an opportunity to develop my music skills. _____ , I will meet young musicians from all over the world.

4 I play the violin. I _____ play the piano.

5 This course means I can improve my music. _____ I can practise my English.

6 If I play in an orchestra, I will get useful experience. _____ it will be easier for me to get a place at university to study music.

4 Complete the strategies box with the words below.

[reason   addresses ✓   information   interests]

A formal letter of application

• Write the [1] _addresses_ and the date in the correct places.

• Give your [2] _____ for writing in paragraph 1.

• Describe yourself and your background, your studies, your [3] _____ and ambitions.

• Add [4] _____ with linking words such as *In addition, also, As a result.*

• Do not use contracted forms (*I have* NOT *I've*).

• Organise your letter into clear paragraphs to make it easier to understand.

• Don't forget to sign off correctly.

• Check the number of words and then check your grammar, punctuation and spelling.

5 Read the task and then write your letter of application. Use the ideas in exercises 2 and 3 and the strategies in exercise 4 to help you. Write 120–150 words.

> You want to take part in an international music course in England for a month.
> • Describe yourself and your background.
> • Give information about your studies and interests.
> • Describe your ambitions.
> • Give at least two reasons why you want to go on this course.

Speaking

Having a conversation

6 Complete the conversations with the expressions from the box.

[Nice to meet you
I see you like   Sorry?
What do you mean? ✓
Excuse me!   That's amazing!]

1 A: Where are you staying?
  B: _What do you mean?_
  A: Where's your accommodation?

2 A: My name's Helen.
  B: _____ , Helen.

3 A: I love *Coldplay*'s music.
  B: So do I! _____ I listen to them all the time!

4 A: _____
  B: Yes? Can I help you?

5 A: Where are you going?
  B: _____ Can you repeat that?'
  A: Yes … Where are you going?

6 A: I've just bought some new CDs.
  B: Can I look at them? _____ the same music as me.

7 Put the conversation between Laura and Mark in the correct order.

☐ Mark: No, the seat is free, please sit down. I see you like books, what are you reading?

☐ Laura: Sorry? What was that?

☑ Laura: Excuse me! Is anyone sitting here?

☐ Laura: *Northern Lights* … it's by Philip Pullman.

☐ Mark: Nice to meet you, Laura. I'm Mark.

☐ Mark: Seriously? He's my favourite writer! That's amazing. Have you read *The Amber Spyglass*?

☐ Mark: *The Amber Spyglass* … it's another book by Philip Pullman.

☐ Laura: No, I haven't read it. Anyway, my name's Laura.

Vocabulary

Sporting activities

1 **Underline** the correct verbs to complete the dialogue.

A: I need to [1] *get/go* fit. I haven't done any exercise in months.

B: I [2] *do/go* running every evening. Would you like to go with me?

A: Really?

B: Yes, I want to [3] *enter/lose* a competition this spring.

A: That's great, but … I don't know … what if I [4] *get/go* injured?

B: Injured? Jogging around a park? Well, you can [5] *join/get* a gym instead if you like.

A: I don't like gyms … there are too many people and the exercises are boring.

B: You don't really want to do a sport, do you?

A: Perhaps not … but I [6] *support/beat* our local basketball team!

2 **Complete the text with the words from the box.**

[best   goal   injured   match (x2)   team ✓]

"We're in the eighty-fifth minute of the final match of the inter-school cup and it's Slough High versus Maidenhead School. The score is two all. We've got five minutes left to beat the other [1] _team_ and win the [2] _____ . Sam Wood has got the ball … come on, Sam! Oh, no! He's fallen over! Is he okay? So far, nobody's got [3] _____ in this tournament. Now Maidenhead's Tim Brooke has got the ball … and he scores a beautiful [4] _____ ! And here's the referee's whistle! It's over! Slough have lost the [5] _____ ! Still, let's thank them for doing their [6] _____ ."

Grammar

Defining relative clauses

3 (*) **Match the three parts of each sentence.**

Tennis is ———— a person ———— **whose** job is to defend the goal.

The goalkeeper is — a place — **which** requires speed and general fitness.

A pool is —— a game —— **who** teaches you how to play a sport.

An instructor is   the footballer   **where** you go swimming

4 (*) **Underline** the correct relative pronoun to complete the sentences.

1 Yesterday, I met a girl *who/which* was in my class in primary school.

2 I bought a stopwatch *which/whose* broke after a week.

3 This is the house *which/where* we lived when I was a child.

4 I'm phoning the person *whose/who* car is parked in front of the gate.

5 The shop *where/which* I bought my table tennis bat is closed today.

5 (**) **Complete the email with *who*, *which*, *where* or *whose*.**

To: naughton_fl@hotmail.com
From: jessie_n16@gmail.com
Subject: Hi

Hi Mum and Dad,

I'm enjoying myself at the sports camp. Here is a photo. It shows the court [1] _where_ we play tennis. On the court you can see Rachel, the girl [2] _____ I play with most of the time. Next to her is Shelley, the girl [3] _____ racquet I borrowed last week when I broke mine.

There is a swimming pool [4] _____ we swim every morning. The boys [5] _____ we swim with are Rachel's brother Dave and his friend Tom. Tom's got a friend [6] _____ sister is a kickboxer. I think that's so cool. I'd like to try a sport [7] _____ not many girls do. What do you think?

Lots of love,

Jessie xxxxx

6 (✱✱✱) **Complete the second sentence so that it means the same as the first. Use *who, which, whose* or *where*.**

1 A player got injured in yesterday's match. He is now in hospital.

The player *who got injured in yesterday's match* is now in hospital.

2 We were planning to use a classmate's ball for the match. He's not here.

The classmate _____ _____ is not here.

3 Mike got a present. He liked it very much.

Mike got a present _____ very much.

4 He was born in a small town. It had no football stadium.

The small town _____ _____ had no football stadium.

5 A woman answered the phone. She had a strange voice.

The woman _____ _____ had a strange voice.

7 (✱✱) **Cross out the relative pronouns *who, which* or *that* wherever possible.**

1 This is the house ~~that~~ our grandfather built.

2 They live in a house which looks a bit like a castle.

3 All the money that we had was stolen last night.

4 Alice is the only person that understands me.

5 Chris is the only person who I trust.

Grammar Plus: Reduced relative clauses

8 (✱✱✱) **Complete the second sentence using reduced relative clauses.**

1 I saw a man who was wearing an FC Barcelona football shirt.

I saw a man *wearing an FC Barcelona football shirt* .

2 The new gym that was built last year is better than the old one.

The new gym _____ _____ is better than the old one.

3 There was a family that had five children in the park.

There was a family _____ _____ in the park.

4 Can you see the car which is coming up the road?

Can you see the car _____ ?

5 Bill is the man who's got blue eyes and a warm smile.

Bill is the man _____ .

Grammar reference

Defining relative clauses

Relative clauses give information about the subject or object of a main clause. We begin a relative clause with a relative pronoun.

A Sat-Nav is a computer device	*which*	*can direct you to a destination.*
[main clause]	[relative pronoun]	[relative clause]

Relative pronouns: *who, which, that, where, whose*

- We use *who* or *that* for people:

*That's the man **who/that** sold me his car.*

- We use *which* or *that* for things:

*A dictionary is a book **which/that** explains the meaning of words.*

- We use *where* for places:

*This is the place **where** I saw Robert for the first time.*

- We use *whose* for possession/belonging.

*Jessica is going out with a boy **whose** brother is a swimming champion.*

Omitting the relative pronoun

We can omit a relative pronoun when it is the object of a sentence:

*This is the picture (~~which/that~~) **Martin** painted last week.*
*I quite like the girl (~~who/that~~) **you** have invited to the party.*

We cannot omit a relative pronoun when it is the subject:

*A scientist is a person **who** asks questions and tries different ways to answer them.* (we cannot omit *who*)
*I won't ask Hannah anything **which** could embarrass her.* (we cannot omit *which*)

Reduced relative clauses

We can reduce relative clauses by omitting the relative pronoun (*who, that* or *which*) and the auxiliary verb *be* (*is/are/was/were*):

*Do you know the woman **who is** talking to Nick?* →
Do you know the woman talking to Nick?

*The player **that was** injured during the match was our best striker.* → *The player injured during the match was our best striker.*

When we talk about physical characteristics and possession, we can use *with* instead of the relative pronoun (*who* or *that*) and the auxiliary verb *have*:

*Have you seen the girl **who has** long curly hair?* →
*Have you seen the girl **with** long curly hair?*

*People **who had** small children boarded the plane first.* →
*People **with** small children boarded the plane first.*

2

Vocabulary

Likes and dislikes

1 Mark these statements + (like), – (dislike) or +/– (neutral).

1 *I love going to football matches.* `+`

2 *I can't stand team games.* ☐

3 *I don't mind volleyball.* ☐

4 *I can't see the point of watching sport on TV.* ☐

5 *I find swimming boring.* ☐

6 *I'm really passionate about biking.* ☐

7 *I quite enjoy tennis.* ☐

8 *I'm really into surfing.* ☐

9 *I'm not really into football.* ☐

2 Complete the text with the words from the box.

> about   into ✓   of   enjoys   finds
> mind   stand

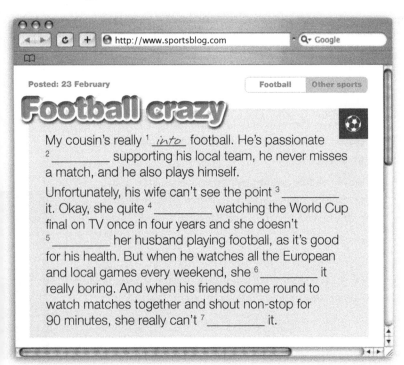

Posted: 23 February   Football | Other sports

Football crazy

My cousin's really ¹ _into_ football. He's passionate ² _____ supporting his local team, he never misses a match, and he also plays himself.

Unfortunately, his wife can't see the point ³ _____ it. Okay, she quite ⁴ _____ watching the World Cup final on TV once in four years and she doesn't ⁵ _____ her husband playing football, as it's good for his health. But when he watches all the European and local games every weekend, she ⁶ _____ it really boring. And when his friends come round to watch matches together and shout non-stop for 90 minutes, she really can't ⁷ _____ it.

Grammar

Present perfect and past simple

3 (✱) Complete the questions and answers with the present perfect form of the verbs in brackets.

1 A: _Has anyone seen Helen recently_ (anyone/see Helen) recently?

   B: Yes, she was here a moment ago. _She's just left_ (she/just/leave).

2 A: _____ (you/ever/play) baseball?

   B: No. Actually, I _____ (never/understand) the rules.

3 A: _____ (Paul/arrive) yet?

   B: No, but _____ (he/just/phone). He's on his way.

4 A: _____ (you/see) my swimming things?

   B: I _____ (already/tell) you. They're in the bathroom.

5 A: Are you still using my pen or can I have it back?

   B: Just a second … I _____ (not/finish) yet.

4 (✱✱) Complete the sentences with the words from the box.

> ago   at   in   last   one   when ✓

1 Jack started running _when_ he was still in primary school.

2 He and his dad went running in the park _____ 6 a.m. every day.

3 _____ day, he met the coach of a local athletics club.

4 He joined the club _____ 2006.

5 Two years _____ he won his first international race.

6 _____ month he was chosen for the Olympic team.

5 (✱✱) Underline the correct form to complete the sentences.

1 In 2006, my father *has taken/took* me to Berlin to see one of the World Cup matches.

2 *I've been/I went* to Spain five times before.

3 *Have you seen/Did you see* George yesterday?

4 Julie *lost/has lost* her passport! She can't get on the plane without it.

5 *I met/I've met* some really great people in France last year.

6 Three years ago I *didn't know/haven't known* how to play squash.

7 The players *just came out/have just come out* of the dressing room.

8 Veronica *has become/became* interested in Taekwondo when she was fifteen.

6 (✱✱✱) Complete the text with the correct form (present perfect or past simple) of the verbs in brackets.

✕

PELÉ
The most famous footballer of all time

Born 1940, Três Corações, Brazil

| Full biography | List of clubs | Career statistics | Trivia |

Did you know that ...?
★ ★

★ He ¹ _was born_ (be born) into a poor family and as a boy he ² _____ (not have) a proper football. He and his friends ³ _____ (play) with a sock stuffed with old newspapers or with a grapefruit.

★ In the twenty years of his football career, he ⁴ _____ (score) a total of 1,281 goals – more than any other professional footballer.

★ He ⁵ _____ (play) for the Brazilian team in three World Cups.

★ On 7 July 1957, in a match against Argentina, he ⁶ _____ (become) the youngest player to score in an international game.

★ In 1958, he ⁷ _____ (be) the youngest player to play in a World Cup final.

★ When he ⁸ _____ (score) his 1,000th goal in 1969, he ⁹ _____ (dedicate) it to the poor children of Brazil.

★ He ¹⁰ _____ (write) several autobiographies.

★ He ¹¹ _____ (appear) in thirteen films.

★ Since his retirement, he ¹² _____ (be) an ambassador for various international organisations.

Grammar reference

Present perfect and past simple

Use of the present perfect

We use the present perfect to talk about actions or situations which happened not long ago and have results/consequences now:

*Mark **has** just **won** a gold medal in the 100m breast stroke!* (and that's why he's happy now)

We also use the present perfect to talk about actions or events which happened in the past, but we don't know or we are not interested in when exactly they happened:

*My uncle **has been** to America four times.* (in his life, it doesn't matter when exactly)
***Have** you ever **eaten** Spanish omelette?* (it is not important when)

Time expressions with the present perfect

We often use the present perfect with time expressions such as:

already, yet, just, never, ever, recently

Use of the past simple

We use the past simple to talk about actions or events which happened at a definite time in the past:

*We **went** to the zoo **last Tuesday**.*
***When my grandfather was young** he **lived** in Argentina.*

Time expressions with the past simple

We often use the past simple with time expressions such as:

yesterday (morning/evening)
the day before yesterday
last (year/month/week/Saturday/night)
in (February/1999/the 1960s)
at (10 o'clock/3.30/midnight)
(three days/a week/fifteen years) ago
when I was (ten/young)
one (day/afternoon)
on (Tuesday, 2nd June, my birthday)

Notice!
We do not use the present perfect with a definite time.

*I **visited** many interesting museums **last year**.* ✓
NOT: *I ~~have visited~~ many interesting museums **last year**.*

13

2

Vocabulary

Sports competitions

1 Read the text. Choose the best word, a, b or c to complete the gaps in the text.

BASKETBALL

Did you know that James Naismith ¹ _a_ the rules of basketball in 1891? It quickly ² ____ all over the world and now it is now a popular sport in many countries. It became an Olympic sport in 1936 and the US has ³ ____ the most gold medals so far. Michael Jordan ⁴ ____ a champion in the 1990s and he's still one of the most famous players ever.

Before he retired, he ⁵ ____ many records and his average of 31.5 baskets a game is the best in NBA history. Every year, thousands of American schools ⁶ ____ basketball competitions and students compete in local leagues.

1	a developed ✓	b broke	c decided
2	a travelled	b went	c spread
3	a held	b won	c played
4	a developed	b became	c won
5	a broke	b changed	c started
6	a hold	b throw	c catch

2 Complete the table with the correct verb or noun form.

Verb	Noun
¹ _develop_	development
injure	² _____
achieve	³ _____
⁴ _____	invention
record	⁵ _____
compete	⁶ _____
⁷ _____	training

3 Complete the sentences with the correct verb or noun from exercise 2.

1 He _injured_ his leg when he fell over and had to go to hospital.
2 Michael Phelps holds the Olympic _____ for the most medals in swimming.
3 We're playing in a tennis _____ tomorrow.
4 She was given a special medal for all her _____ in sport.
5 I think the English _____ the game of football, but I'm not sure.
6 You have to do a lot of _____ before a marathon.

Reading

4 Look at texts A and B quickly and choose the best answer.

1 Text A is
  a a newspaper article
  b a biography
2 Text B is from
  a an encyclopedia
  b a sports magazine

5 Read Text A carefully and match five of the sentences a–f to the correct place 1–5 in the text. There is one extra sentence.

a Her first big achievement was winning the 100 metres at the age of fifteen in the Welsh Junior National Games.

b Tanni Grey Thompson is an incredible person and many people admire her.

c Then she went to Loughborough University and got a degree in Politics and Social Administration.

d She is also active in various charities, including Sportsleaders UK and the Sport for Good Foundation.

e They have one daughter, Carys.

f In 2000 she came third in the BBC Sports Personality of the Year.

(A)

Dame* Tanni Carys Davina Grey-Thompson

born 26 July, Cardiff, Wales

Biography

Dame Tanni Carys Davina Grey-Thompson is a Welsh athlete and TV presenter. Grey-Thompson was born with spina bifida* and she uses a wheelchair. However, she has overcome her disability to become one of the most successful and popular athletes in Britain.

Grey-Thompson went to St Cyres Comprehensive School, Penarth, near Cardiff. ¹ ____

When she was young, Grey-Thompson tried basketball and swimming. Although she enjoyed these sports, she became more interested in athletics after watching the London Marathon on TV. ² ____ In 1988 she won a bronze medal for the 400m at the Seoul Paralympic Games. Since then, she has won fifteen more Paralympic medals, including eleven gold medals – and thirteen World Championship Medals. She also holds over thirty world records and she won the London Wheelchair Marathon six times between 1992 and 2002.

6 Read Text B carefully. Tick (✓) true or cross (✗) false for the statements below.

1 ☐ Tanni makes clothes for disabled children.
2 ☐ Tanni competed in the Paralympic Games in Athens.
3 ☐ Tanni won an important sports award in 2000.
4 ☐ Tanni complained to the BBC because she couldn't get onto the stage in her wheelchair.

7 Read both texts again and choose the correct answers.

1 Tanni became interested in athletics
  a because she didn't like other sports such as swimming.
  b after she saw a sports competition on television.
  c because she couldn't play basketball.

2 In total she has won ___ Paralympic Medals.
  a 13   b 15   c 16

3 Now, Tanni
  a is still competing in competitions.
  b is training for the World Cup in Manchester.
  c does not compete professionally any more.

4 X-Ray is
  a the television programme that Tanni has presented.
  b a TV programme that not many people watch.
  c a computer programme, not a TV programme.

5 The name 'Tanni' is a nickname that she got because her sister
  a couldn't pronounce her name 'Carys' correctly.
  b thought she was very small when she was born.
  c was smaller than her when she was born.

6 When she was made a member of the World Sports Academy, Tanni
  a was extremely pleased.
  b admired the sports star Michael Jordan.
  c didn't think it was very important.

(B)

DID YOU KNOW ... ?

* Tanni Grey-Thompson was originally called 'Carys'. When she was born, her sister called her 'tiny' because she was very, very small. This is how she got her nickname 'Tanni'.
* Her daughter Carys thinks athletics is boring. She says, 'But mummy, you go round and round in circles!'
* Tanni works as an advisor to a company that makes clothes for disabled children.
* She competed in the Paralympic Games in Seoul, Barcelona, Atlanta, Sydney and Athens.
* She says one of her proudest moments was when she was chosen as a member of the World Sport Academy – it includes sports legends such as Pelé and Michael Jordan.
* She was unable to accept her award for BBC Sports Personality of the Year in 2000 because she couldn't get up onto the stage in her wheelchair. Hundreds of viewers complained, but Tanni said she wasn't angry about the mistake.
* Her favourite food is fish and chips!
* She and her husband have identical tattoos on their right feet.

³ ___ In addition, she has won BBC Wales Sports Personality of the Year three times, in 1992, 2000 and 2004. In 1992 she received an MBE* and in 2000 the Queen awarded her an OBE*, both for services to sport. She was made Dame in 2005.

Although she retired from competitive sport in 2007 after the Paralympic World Cup in Manchester, Grey-Thompson remains a public figure. She has presented the popular BBC Wales TV consumer programme X-Ray. ⁴ ___ Grey-Thompson is now one of the organisers of the London Marathon.

She is married to Dr Ian Thompson. ⁵ ___

* Dame is a title for a woman who the British government has given a special honour to
* spina bifida is a medical condition that affects the back bone
* MBE (Member of the British Empire) and OBE (Order of the British Empire) are medals that the Queen gives for special services to the country

Reading

True/False/No information

1 Read the beginning of the article, A Countryside Education and the statements 1–3. Tick (✓) true, cross (✗) false or write (?) if there is no information. Then read a student's notes for each statement and complete them with information from the text.

A Countryside Education

When people hear that Oliver Martin doesn't go to school, some of them are surprised. Oliver, 17, is one of approximately 20,000 children and young people in the UK who are educated at home. And for Oliver home is a farm in Yorkshire, where his parents run a riding club. Ever since he was five, he's spent most of his time with horses. You might say, 'But that's not education!' Oliver is confident, however, that he's learning all sorts of things: Biology, Geography, History, English, and useful life skills besides. Today he shares his experience with us.

1 ☐ Oliver lives on a farm.
   The text says 'for Oliver _____ in Yorkshire.'

2 ☐ Horses are the only animals on the farm.
   The text mentions only _____ but there could be other animals.

3 ☐ Oliver studies a lot of subjects at school.
   The text says he's learning _____ but it also says 'Oliver Martin _____ go to school'.

2 Match the sentence beginnings 1–3 and endings a–c to create the exam tip.

> **Exam TIP**
>
> 1 A statement is true when
> 2 A statement is false when
> 3 We can say there is no information when
>
> a the statement and the text say things which cannot both be true at the same time.
> b the statement could be true, but the text does not say so.
> c the text says the same thing in other words.

3 Read the second paragraph of the article and the statements below. Tick (✓) true, cross (✗) false or write (?) if there is *no information* in the text. Underline the sentence or phrase which helped you to choose each answer.

I've been riding since I was six, and now I take part in competitions. I also know how to look after and train a horse. And that's not the same as looking after a bicycle; a horse is alive and has its own opinions. I've also helped with sick and injured horses a lot; I could probably work as a vet's assistant now.

1 ☐ Oliver has won some riding competitions.
2 ☐ Looking after a horse is more difficult than looking after a bicycle.
3 ☐ Oliver works as a vet's assistant.

4 Read the rest of the article and the statements below. Tick (✓) true, cross (✗) false or write (?) if there is *no information* in the text.

I've learned a lot of geography from riding, both on my own and with customers. I know every riding trail in Yorkshire, and I could get from here to Scotland on horseback. I also read a lot about local history. Last year I did a project on places connected with writers in Yorkshire, with my own photos. A short version is now on our club's website. I like literature and I'm doing an A-level in English as an independent student.

The great thing is that everything I do happens in the real world. On a farm you have responsibilities that are serious: you can't forget to feed animals and just say 'Sorry, Miss, I forgot.' When I take a group of riders out I'm also responsible for them. I have to take care of them and make sure they don't do anything dangerous. That's probably the most difficult skill I've learned: working with people.

1 ☐ Oliver learns geography from books.
2 ☐ Oliver isn't interested in world history.
3 ☐ Oliver's history project was connected with literature.
4 ☐ Parts of Oliver's history project are on the internet.
5 ☐ Oliver has never forgotten to feed the animals.
6 ☐ Working with people is easier than studying.

Listening

Matching

5 a In exercise 5b you will hear a young woman talking about the sports she did at school. Before you listen, read statements A–C and think *why* a person might say these things about sports at school. Match the statements A–C to the possible reasons 1–3.

A I became interested in volleyball through a friend.

B I enjoyed PE more than other subjects.

C I became especially good at one sport.

1 ☐ Because I'm very active and I don't like sitting down.

2 ☐ Because our school specialised in it.

3 ☐ Because I liked watching her play.

b ③ Listen twice to a young woman talking about the sports she did at school. From the statements A–C in exercise 5a choose the one which best summarises what she says.

Speaker 1: Statement ___

Exam TIP

Before you listen, read the questions or statements carefully and think about what the speakers might say.

6 ④ Listen to three other people talking about the sports they did at school. Match the statements D–G to the speakers 2–4. There is one extra statement.

D I didn't enjoy the sports that were available at my school.

E I learned one sport very well at school.

F I found most sports boring.

G I can't see the point of competitive sports.

Speaker 2: Statement ___

Speaker 3: Statement ___

Speaker 4: Statement ___

Use of English

Gap fill

7 Match the words 1–6 with words a–f to make collocations.

1	pass/fail	a	in
2	primary/private	b	goals
3	set (yourself)	c	an exam
4	go	d	(good/bad) marks
5	get	e	swimming/running
6	specialise	f	school

8 Put the collocations from exercise 7 in the categories below.

verb + noun   *1c* ___ ___   verb + *ing* form   ___

verb + preposition   ___   adjective + noun   ___

9 a What part of speech do you need in each gap: noun (n.), verb (v.), adjective (adj.) or preposition (prep.)?

1 I went to a ___ school which was very expensive.   *adj.*

2 Mark goes ___ every morning before school.   ___

3 Kate is unhappy because she ___ an important exam yesterday.   ___

4 Our school specialises ___ art subjects.   ___

5 You must to learn to set yourself ___ which you can achieve.   ___

b Complete the gaps with words from exercise 7.

Exam TIP

Learn collocations. The missing words in a gap-fill exercise often form collocations with the words before or after the gap.

10 Read a description of a favourite teacher. Complete the text with the words below. There is one extra word.

about   get   pass   primary ✓
set   walking   who   worth

My best teacher ever

My favourite teacher was Miss Crewdson – my class teacher in
¹ *primary* school. She was the person ² _____ taught me to enjoy learning. She read aloud to us and then gave us books that were ³ _____ reading. She talked ⁴ _____ Maths in an interesting way, using funny examples. Some days instead of sitting in class we went ⁵ _____ in the park and looked at trees and birds. In Miss Crewdson's class, it was more important to learn and have fun than to ⁶ _____ good marks in exams. She even taught me to ⁷ _____ myself goals; often just small ones, such as 'to learn to write my name beautifully'. I'll always remember Miss Crewdson.

Vocabulary & Grammar

1 Cross out the word or phrase that you cannot use with the words in bold.

1 **get** the sack/~~skills~~/a pay rise
2 beat/support/enter **the other team**
3 **win** a match/a race/a goal
4 **make** sense/goals/decisions
5 state/optional/compulsory **subjects**
6 **get** your best/injured/fit
7 pass/revise/fail **an exam**

/6

2 Complete the sentences with one word in each gap.

1 _Private_ schools in England are very expensive.
2 John's really passionate _____ football. He wants to be a professional footballer.
3 I have no idea how to play cricket – the _____ are too complicated for me.
4 Gina's studying to be a doctor but she hasn't chosen the area of medicine she wants to _____ in yet.
5 I think she earns quite a high _____ in her new job.
6 I _____ playing chess a bit boring.
7 My uncle has a successful _____ as an actor, writer and director in theatre and television.

/6

3 Complete the sentences with the correct form of the verbs in brackets. Use the present simple, present continuous, present perfect or past simple tense.

1 Fiona _has been_ to America three times.
2 What time _____ (they/come) home yesterday?
3 That dress _____ (look) really nice on you, Joan.
4 I _____ (not/see) their new show yet.
5 Tom, listen to me! What _____ (you/think) about … ?
6 I _____ (go) to Disneyland when I was eight.
7 My best friend _____ (get) married next month.
8 Ian _____ (not/want) to be a teacher.

/7

4 Match the beginnings of the sentences 1–6 with the endings a–f using correct relative pronouns. Make any necessary changes and omit the pronouns where possible.

1 A vet is a person …
2 This is the place …
3 The police are looking for the woman …
4 I didn't like the meal …
5 A Sat-Nav is an electronic device …
6 I don't like teachers …

a Her fingerprints were on the gun.
b They give a lot of homework.
c She cooked it for us yesterday.
d I saw her here for the first time.
e He/She treats animals.
f It helps people to find their way.

1 _A vet is a person who treats animals._
2 _____
3 _____
4 _____
5 _____
6 _____

/5

5 Complete the blog entry with one word in each gap.

http://www.hatesblog.com   Google

Posted: 25 March   Home   Friends

SPORT? – Not for me!

To say that I'm not really [1] _into_ sport is just not enough. I hate it! And, in particular, I can't [2] _____ team games like football. When you think about it – what is it all about? Twenty-two people [3] _____ run on the pitch kicking the ball. I can't really see the [4] _____ of it. To be honest, I [5] _____ never been good at sport. That's probably why I hate it so much. But does everybody need to be sporty? After finishing school, I'm going to get a [6] _____ in education and teach [7] _____ a school. And, obviously, I'm [8] _____ planning to teach Physical Education!

/7

Listening

6 (5) Listen to the radio programme *What's new in education?*. Answer the questions with the names of three speakers (Ann, Robert or Grace).

Who:

1 has just started learning at home? _____

2 has improved academically? _____

3 at first didn't like the idea of home schooling? _____

4 finds the experience of learning at home quite lonely? _____

5 enjoys learning Maths? _____

/5

Reading

7 Read the newspaper article. Tick true (✓) or cross (✗) false or write (?) if there is no information.

chool cricket anged my life'

onty Panesar is a hero to many young cricket fans. He is a member of the England cricket n and one of the best bowlers in world. Cricket has been part of nty's life since he was a young oolboy. This is why he has recently en his support to an exciting new ket programme for state schools in gland and Wales.

he programme, called Chance to ne, was started by the Cricket ndation in 2005. When it began, y one in ten state schools played petitive cricket. Its aim is to get dren playing cricket in a third of all e primary and secondary schools. programme gives school children chance to learn the game and play ular matches against other schools. as already reached more than 70,000 dren and aims to reach more than

two million by the time the programme comes to an end in 2015.

Monty explained that being a good cricketer changed his life in school, and helped him to grow up. 'Playing for my school cricket team made a huge difference to my school life,' he said. 'For the first time, I knew people in the years above me and from the other schools in my area. It widened my social circle and helped me to get to know and respect lots of people.' Monty added, 'When I was younger I benefited from Kwik Cricket and I think the game needs initiatives such as Kwik Cricket and Urban Cricket to encourage kids to play.'

Chance to Shine is also providing links to schools overseas. Monty Panesar has recently launched Chance to Shine's Anglo-Indian links, bringing together 100 schools in the UK with schools in India. 'It will help the children understand life in each other's country through projects and lessons based on a shared love of cricket,' Panesar said.

1 Monty Panesar has helped Chance to Shine financially.

2 At the beginning of the programme cricket was played in 33% of state schools.

3 The programme has already started in some schools in England.

4 Playing cricket changed Panesar's life at school because he met a lot of people.

5 Panesar has never played Kwik Cricket.

6 Panesar is planning to launch the programme in many countries.

/6

Communication

8 Complete the dialogues with one word in each gap.

1 A: E _xcuse_ me! I think you've dropped your glasses.

   B: Oh yes, thank you very much.

2 A: My name's Sam.

   B: Nice to m_____ you, Sam. I'm Olivia.

3 A: I actually spoke to Beyoncé.

   B: S_____ ? That's amazing!

4 A: I love classical music … well, sort of … I'm not really into it …

   B: What do you m_____ ? I don't quite understand.

/3

9 Match six of the questions 1–7 with answers a–f. There is one extra question that you do not need.

1 What sport does he do?

2 Where was he born?

3 When did he start playing basketball?

4 Did he train a lot when he was at school?

5 Has he broken any records?

6 Has he won any competitions?

7 What are his hopes for the future?

a Yes, he's been the county champion three times.

b When he was in primary school.

c In Malaga.

d No, not really. Only twice a week.

e He wants to play in the Olympics.

f He plays basketball.

/5

Marks

Vocabulary & Grammar	**/31 marks**
Listening	**/5 marks**
Reading	**/6 marks**
Communication	**/8 marks**
Total:	**/50 marks**

self assessment test 1

19

3 family matters

* easy to do
** a bit harder
*** extra challenge

Vocabulary

Physical description

1 Match the words 1–6 which cannot describe the same person as the words a–f.

1 in her teens   a short
2 scruffy   b slim
3 tall   c straight hair
4 plump   d dark hair
5 wavy hair   e middle-aged
6 blonde hair   f glamorous

2 Read the descriptions of Mike, Paul and Richard and look at the picture. Identify the family members, then write in the missing letters to complete the sentences about Paul and Richard.

Mike and Paul are brothers. They are both in their teens, but they look completely different. Mike is tall and thin, with dark wavy hair. He looks rather scruffy.

Paul is [1] s _hort_ and slightly [2] p _ _ _ p, with a [3] r _ _ _ d face, but he looks really [4] s _ _ _ t because of his clothes. His hair is [5] st _ _ _ _ _ t and [6] f _ _ r.

Their father, Richard, is [7] m _ _ _ _ _ - _ _ _ d. He's [8] t _ _ _ and quite good-looking, but he's going [9] b _ _ _ .

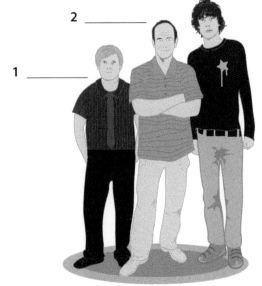

2 _____

1 _____

3 _____

Grammar

Making comparisons

3 (*) Build the comparative and superlative forms of these adjectives.

	Comparative	Superlative
dark	*darker*	*the darkest*
fine		
slim		
tidy		
elegant		
bad		

4 a (**) Complete Sarah's thoughts with comparative and superlative forms of the adjectives in italics.

Who should I go out with? Chris is *tall* and *good-looking*. Alex is slightly [1] _taller_ and [2] _better-looking_ than Chris. Mike is the [3] _____ and [4] _____ of the three. Alex is *intelligent*. Mike is a lot [5] _____ than Alex. And Chris is the [6] _____ . Mike's got a *good* car. Chris's car is [7] _____ than Mike's. But Alex has got by far the [8] _____ car in our town.

b (**) Complete Sarah's conclusion with the words from. the box.

> less   as ✓   as   than   much

I think I'll go out with Bill. He's not [1] _as_ good-looking [2] _____ Chris, he's [3] _____ intelligent than Alex although he hasn't even got a car! But he's [4] _____ kinder and more responsible [5] _____ all three of them.

5 (✱✱) Read what Sam says about his family. Write their names under the pictures.

a Eva is slightly taller than me.

b Frank is by far the tallest of us all.

c Daniel is a little shorter than me.

d Ruby is a lot shorter than me.

e Jack is much taller than me.

| ① | ② | ③ | ④ | ⑤ | ⑥ |

_____ _me___ _____ _____ _____ _____

6 (✱✱✱) Complete the second sentence so that it means the same as the first. Use the word given in bold.

1 Tom is more talkative than Julia. **as**

Julia is _not as talkative as_ Tom.

2 Life in the city is more exciting than life in the country. **less**

Life in the country _____ _____ life in the city.

3 Women are different from men. **same**

Women are not _____ _____ men.

4 My brother's hair is a bit like mine. **similar**

My brother's hair _____ _____ mine.

5 Gail is not like her sister. **from**

Gail is _____ her sister.

6 Christine is slimmer than Lynn. **as**

Lynn is _____ Christine.

Grammar reference

Making comparisons

Form

	Adjectives	Comparatives	Superlatives
One syllable	short clean	short**er** clean**er**	the short**est** the clean**est**
One syllable, ending in -e	wide cute	wid**er** cut**er**	the wid**est** the cut**est**
One syllable, ending in one consonant	big slim	big**ger** slim**mer**	the big**gest** the slim**mest**
Ending in -y	dry pretty	dri**er** pretti**er**	the dri**est** the pretti**est**
Two and three or more syllables	responsible modest	**more/less** responsible **more/less** modest	the most/the least responsible the most/the least modest
Irregular	good bad	**better** **worse**	the best the worst

Use of comparative adjectives

We use the comparative form (+ _than_) to compare two things, people or groups of things or people:

My shirt was **more expensive** than Robert's.

We usually use an object pronoun after _than_ (_me, you, him, her, it, us, them_).

He is stronger **than me**.

Use of superlative adjectives

We use the superlative form to compare more than two things, people or groups. We normally use _the_ before a superlative. After a superlative we can use _in_ or _of_. We use _in_ with the names of places or groups:

My uncle Pete is **the tallest** person **in** our family.
Crows are believed to be **the most intelligent of** all birds.

Describing small and big differences

When we want to describe a small difference, we can use _a little, slightly_ or _a bit_ before a comparative adjective:

Her hair is **a little longer** than mine.
Jack's new car is **slightly bigger** than mine.
My new shoes were **a bit more expensive** than the old ones.

When we want to describe a big difference, we can use _much_ or _a lot_ before a comparative adjective. We can use _by far_ before a superlative adjective:

The book is **much more interesting** than the film.
The red dress is **a lot cheaper** than the blue one.
This is **by far the fastest** car in the world.

Other useful phrases for comparing

• _different from_

My school is **different from** yours.

• _similar to_

Your school report is very **similar to** mine.

• _the same as_

My shoe size is **the same as** my sister's.

Vocabulary

Describing people

1 Match the sentence beginnings 1–6 with the endings a–f.

1 Dominant people
2 Sociable people
3 Shy people
4 Argumentative people
5 Popular people
6 Sensitive people

a are not confident.
b often disagree with others.
c are well liked by others.
d may cry more easily than others.
e like the company of other people.
f tell others what to do.

2 Complete the text with words which describe appearance or personality.

These are my classmates. The one with
¹f r e c k l e s and ²l _ _ _ brown hair is Jessica.
She's got a very strong ³p _ _ _ _ _ _ _ _ _ and
she can be quite ⁴d _ _ _ _ _ _ _ : she likes telling
people what to do. The big guy's Dave. He's 190 cm
⁵t _ _ _ . He's very ⁶s _ _ _ _ _ _ _ : he loves hanging
out with friends more than anything in the world.
I don't like Chloe very much; she can be quite
⁷a _ _ _ _ _ _ _ _ _ _ _ sometimes and it's difficult
to do things together with her. Alex is a quiet,
⁸s _ _ boy who doesn't talk much. He's also quite
⁹s _ _ _ _ _ _ _ ; for example, he always notices
when someone is unhappy.

Grammar

Questions with *look like*, *be like*, *like*

3 (✱) Match three answers to each question.

1 [b][ ][ ] What does she look like?
2 [ ][ ][ ] What is she like?
3 [ ][ ][ ] What does she like?

a She talks a lot. She's one of the most talkative people I know!
b She's small and slim, with curly blonde hair and freckles.
c I don't really know her very well. She's nice and friendly, but I can't tell you more than that.
d Sports, cooking and parties. And being with her boyfriend!
e She looks very glamorous, like a movie star.
f She's passionate about music. She listens to every kind of music and she's got about 10,000 music files on her computer.
g She's really into horse riding. She spends every weekend riding and looking after her horse.
h Exactly the same as her twin sister – the same height, the same dark hair and green eyes.
i She's very confident, with a really strong personality. She scares me a bit!

4 (✱✱) Use the words in brackets to make questions for the answers.

1 (Richard) *What does Richard like* ?
Maths, music and long-distance running.

2 (your first teacher) _____ ?
She was very nice.

3 (your neighbours) _____ ?
They're terrible, in fact. Very argumentative.

4 (your grandma) _____ ?
She's very good-looking, actually. Tall, slim, and very elegant.

5 (Anne) _____ ?
She's really into dancing.

6 (your twin cousins) _____ ?
They're not similar at all. One is slim and dark, the other plump and blonde.

5 **(✳✳)** Complete the text with one word in each gap.

My little cousin Millie is one of the loveliest children I know. She's just eight years old and she [1] _looks_ like a doll with her delicate pink face, curly hair and big grey eyes. But she's no doll. She [2] _____ very intelligent and she's [3] _____ an extremely strong personality. She usually knows very well what she wants. She's fit and lively and she [4] _____ playing games … but she doesn't [5] _____ losing!

Grammar plus: *look* and *look like*

6 **(✳✳✳)** Complete the dialogues with the correct form of *look* or *look like*.

1 A: She _looks like_ a fashion model: tall, slim and glamorous.
   B: She's much too slim. She _____ healthy at all.

2 A: The new neighbours _____ friendly.
   B: We'll see.

3 A: I'm surprised. You _____ your sister. In fact, you're completely different.
   B: I _____ our Mum, and Millie _____ our grandma. When she was young, I mean.

4 A: You _____ tired. Are you okay?
   B: Yes, I'm fine, I'm just working too much. Do I _____ that bad?

5 A: Hey, that new boy _____ Mark Wahlberg.
   B: Are you joking? He _____ younger than my fourteen-year-old brother. And why do you want all boys to _____ movie stars anyway? They're much nicer if they're just normal!

Grammar reference

Questions with *look like, be like, like*

We use *look like* to ask about appearance:

*What **does** she **look like**?* → *She's tall and slim. She's **got** brown eyes.*

*What **do** they **look like**?* → *They're short and they've both **got** blonde wavy hair.*

We use *be like* to ask about personality or for a general description:

*What **is** he **like**?* → *He's very talkative. He's **got** a strong personality.*

*What **are** they **like**?* → *They're confident and easy-going.*

We use *like* to ask about likes/dislikes and people's tastes:

*What **does** she **like**?* → *She **likes** listening to jazz. She **doesn't like** football.*

*What **do** they **like**?* → *They **like** Chinese food. They **don't like** dancing.*

look and *look like*

We can use *look* + adjective to talk about appearance:

*He **looks** very **sleepy** today.*
*You **look great** in that jacket.*

We use *look like* + noun/an object pronoun/ person to talk about similarities:

*Do you think owners **look like their pets**?* (noun)
*My sister **doesn't look like me** at all.* (object pronoun)
*His new girlfriend **looks like Julia Roberts**.* (person)

Vocabulary

Personality

1 Complete the text with the words from the box.

> punctual bossy ✓ sensitive dynamic
> self-centred ambitious organised
> easy-going indecisive conscientious

✕

teenage bloggers

I've got a sister and a brother. My brother, Peter, is older than me and he's really ¹ _bossy_ – he's always telling me what to do! But he's fun to be with because he's very ² _____ – he's got lots of energy and great ideas about things to do. Sometimes his plans go very wrong because he isn't very ³ _____ . He never plans things carefully. Of course, he's always late – he isn't ⁴ _____ at all! He thinks about himself a lot of the time, so he can be a bit ⁵ _____ ,

My younger sister, Kate, is very different. She can be difficult because she gets upset easily – I suppose she's very ⁶ _____ . Sometimes she takes ages to make her mind up, so she can be ⁷ _____ . She's works very hard and she's very ⁸ _____ . She always does things carefully. I think it's because she's very ⁹ _____ – she wants to be rich and successful in the future!

I'm very calm, relaxed and ¹⁰ _____ . I suppose we're all very different, but we get on well and enjoy doing things together.

2 Write the opposites. Use the correct negative prefix, *un-*, *in-*, *im-* or *dis-*.

1 decisive _indecisive_
2 successful _____
3 tidy _____
4 organised _____
5 polite _____
6 ambitious _____
7 sensitive _____
8 sociable _____
9 punctual _____
10 dynamic _____

Listening

3 Look at the cartoon and match the questions 1–3 with the answers a–c.

1 What does your boyfriend look like? ☐

a Sport and music.

2 What is he like? ☐

b He's tall and good-lookin

3 What does he like? ☐

c He's sociable.

4 Look at the cartoon in exercise 3 again. What do you think the interview is about?

a People describing their boyfriend or girlfriend.

b A girl describing how she met her boyfriend.

5 ⑥ Listen to the interview with Rachel and Daniel and choose the correct adjectives for each person. There is one extra word.

> confident shy good-looking beautiful
> argumentative quiet calm easy-going
> sociable

Daniel: _____ , _____ , _____ ,
_____ , _____

Rachel: _____ , _____ , _____

6 ⑥ Listen again. Tick (✓) true or cross (X) false or write (?) if there is no information.

1 ☐ Rachel thinks that Daniel is shy even with people he knows well.

2 ☐ Rachel says that Daniel isn't argumentative because he doesn't like fights.

3 ☐ Daniel hasn't got a very good memory; he can never remember facts.

4 ☐ Rachel thinks people who arrive late are very annoying.

5 ☐ Daniel says that Rachel is more sociable than he is.

6 ☐ Daniel doesn't get all the information about Rachel correct.

Reading

7 Look at the title of the story and the introduction. What sort of story do you think it is?

   1 Science fiction   **2** A mystery

The July Ghost

The extract is from a short story by A.S. Byatt. A man is staying in a house after the break-up of his marriage. He thinks there is something strange about his landlady* because she doesn't speak much and seems sad. It is a hot summer and the man spends a lot of time in the garden. Then he starts to see a boy there. Who is the boy? We never learn the three main characters' names – which adds to the mystery of the story.

*landlady (n) = a woman who owns a house, flat or room that people pay money to live in

---

8 Read the extract and choose the correct answers.

  1 The first time the man sees the boy,
    a the boy is looking for something in the garden.
    b the boy is climbing up a tree.
    c the boy is wearing strange clothes.
    d the man likes the T-shirt the boy is wearing.

  2 When the man speaks to the boy,
    a the boy says something in reply.
    b the boy smiles at the man but says nothing.
    c the boy is really cheeky to the man.
    d the boy stays where he is and watches the man.

  3 The second time the man sees the boy
    a the boy is wearing different clothes.
    b the boy is under the tree.
    c the boy is reading a book in the tree.
    d the boy is in the same place as before.

  4 The third time he sees the boy,
    a the man doesn't notice what he is wearing.
    b the boy is not in the tree.
    c the boy is wearing the trainers as before.
    d the boy speaks to the man for the first time.

  5 When the man describes the boy to his landlady,
    a she reacts immediately.
    b she says he is one of herson's friends.
    c she doesn't say anything for a long time.
    d she says she doesn't knowwho the boy is.

The boy was sitting in a tree. He did not seem to be looking for a ball. He wore blue jeans and trainers, and a brilliant T-shirt, in the colours of a rainbow, which the man on the grass found attractive. He had rather long blond hair, falling over his eyes, so that his face was hidden.

'Hey, you. Do you think you should be up there? It might not be safe.'

The boy looked up and grinned*, and disappeared over the wall. He had a nice grin, friendly not cheeky.

The boy was there again the next day, in the tree, arms crossed. He had on the same T-shirt and jeans. The man watched him, expecting him to move again, but he sat, smiling down pleasantly, and then looking up at the sky. The man read a little, looked up, saw him still there, and said, 'Have you lost anything?'

The child did not reply: after a moment he climbed down a little, hand over hand, dropped to the ground, and then climbed over the wall.

Two days later the boy was lying on his stomach on the grass, this time in a white T-shirt with a design of blue ships, his bare feet and legs stretched in the sun. The man said, 'Hi there,' and the boy looked up, met his look with very blue eyes and smiled.

The man felt reluctant* to tell his landlady about the boy, but when he met him walking out of the kitchen door, spoke to him and got no answer, he wondered if he should speak to her.

The boy was probably a friend of her son's, his landlady said. She looked at him kindly and explained. Her son was killed on the road, two years ago.

'What was the boy like?' she said. 'The one in the house? I don't – talk to his friends. I find it painful. It could be Timmy, or Martin. Maybe they were looking for something, or want …'

He described the boy. Blond, about ten at a guess, very blue eyes, slim, with a rainbow-striped T-shirt and jeans. And the other T-shirt with the ships and wavy lines. And an extraordinary* smile. A really *warm* smile. A good-looking boy.

The man was used to his landlady being silent. But this silence went on* and on and on. She was just staring into the garden. After a time, she said, 'The only thing I want, the only thing I want at all in this world, is to see that boy.'

* grin (v) = to smile showing your teeth (a grin (n) = a big smile)
* reluctant (adj) = not willing to do something
* extraordinary (adj)= very special, wonderful
* go on (v) = continue

A.S. Byatt The July Ghost

Writing

A description of a person

1 In the **introduction**, say who you have chosen and why:
I admire/respect Ellen because …
Someone I admire is …
I would like to be like him/her because …
If it is someone you know, explain how you know the person:
I will always remember Mr Brown, my first English teacher … .

2 In **paragraph 2**, describe his/her life. Make it clear when each thing happened:
At the age of twenty …
When he/she was in his/ her twenties …
Ten years ago …
After (leaving school/he left school) …
While he was working …
Three years later/after …

My Inspiration

My inspiration is my aunt, Mary Davis. She inspires me because she does a dangerous job very well. I also admire her because she's thoughtful – and she's fun to be with.

Mary was born in Inverness in Scotland, but she grew up in Edinburgh. After finishing her university course, she decided to become a fire officer. The training course was difficult. However, she worked very hard and passed the course with top marks. She got her first job with Edinburgh Fire Services. When she was only thirty-five she became the manager of her local fire station.

I think one of her greatest achievements was winning the Fire Officer of the Year award ten years ago. This award is given to people who have shown great bravery in a dangerous situation.

Another reason for admiring her is that she is not only brave, but she is also very talented – she is a fantastic photographer. Furthermore, she is a generous person and spends some of her free time volunteering for a local charity. It's a charity which works with young people who have committed crimes to try to help them learn new skills.

In conclusion, I admire my aunt because she has achieved a lot in her life. I think she is a role model for young people because she has shown that you can be very successful if you work hard and are determined.

3 In **paragraph 3**, give examples of the pe achievements or describe one impor achievement.

4 In **paragraph** 4, say you admire/respect never forget the pe and describe other aspects, such as his personal qualities, hobbies, etc.

5 In the **conclusion**, summarise the rea why you admire/ respect the person:
In conclusion, …
To sum up, …
To conclude, …

1 Read Peter's description and answer the questions. In which paragraph does he

a ☐ describe the person's life?

b ☐ summarise why he admires the person?

c ☐ introduce the person and say why he admires her?

d ☐ talk about her personal qualities and hobbies?

e ☐ describe one important achievement?

2 **a Complete the table with the words below. Are there any words which could go in both columns?**

strong   hard-working   lazy   successful   untidy
argumentative   sociable   confident   thoughtful ✓
talkative   bossy   self-centred   indecisive   organised
dynamic   ambitious

Positive characteristics	Negative characteristics
thoughtful	

b Find four more adjectives in the text which describe positive characteristics. Add them to the table above.

3 Marek has some problems with his essay. Read the task in exercise 5 and Marek's description. Tick (✓) true or cross (✗) false for the statements 1–6 below. Look at the model text on page 26 to help you decide.

```
I would like to be like Mrs Lawson, my first teacher in
primary school. I admire her because she's a strong,
successful person.

She was born in London in 1980 and she's lived there
all her life. She studied at York University. She left
university. She moved to Manchester. She became a
teacher because she likes kids. She works with children
who have learning difficulties. She started that job
when she was in her late twenties.

She's got many interesting hobbies such as sports and
travelling. She raised £2,000 for charity last year –
that was a great achievement.

She works hard and she doesn't let obstacles stop her.
She's dynamic and talented. That's why I admire her.
```

1 ☐ He doesn't divide his essay into clear paragraphs.
2 ☐ He includes all necessary information in his description.
3 ☐ He uses a variety of adjectives to describe the person.
4 ☐ He uses time expressions to show order of events.
5 ☐ He uses an appropriate expression to introduce his conclusion and he explains why he admires the person.
6 ☐ His essay is too short.

4 Complete the strategies box with the words below.

[adjectives   order   information ✓   conclusion]

A personal description

- Read the task carefully. Write notes for all necessary ¹ _information_ you need to include (e.g. why you chose the person, their life and achievements, personal qualities).
- Organise your notes into paragraphs.
- Use a variety of personality ² _____ to make your description interesting. Avoid meaningless adjectives such as good or nice.
- Use time expressions to show the ³ _____ of events clearly.
- Summarise why you admire the person in the ⁴ _____ .
- Check the number of words and then check your grammar, punctuation and spelling.

5 Read the task and then write your description. Use your own ideas or rewrite Marek's description from exercise 3. Use the strategies in exercise 4 to help you. Write 200–250 words.

- Write a description of a person you know that you would like to be like.

Speaking

Making and responding to suggestions

6 Put the conversation a–f between Matt and Kate in the correct order 1–7.

a ☐ Matt: I suppose it's not very exciting. What about *Theatre for all*?

b ☐ Matt: Okay, I've got a better idea, then. What do you think of *The Chameleons*?

c ☐ Kate: I'm not sure about that. I think it's a bit boring.

d ☐ Kate: I think that's a great idea! I love it!

e ☐ Kate: *Theatre for all*? It's not bad, but I think we can do better.

f ☐1 Matt: We need a new name for our theatre group. How about *The Brighton Players*?

g ☐ Matt: Okay, so we agree! Let's go and tell the others.

7 Complete the dialogue with the phrases from the box.

[a better idea   I suppose so
So, do we all agree   That's it
that's a good idea   What about
How about going ✓
I'm not sure about that]

Andy: ¹ _How about going_ for a pizza tonight?

Marie: I think ² _____ .

Chris: We always go for pizza … let's go somewhere else.

Andy: Okay, I've got ³ _____ . We can go to the Indian restaurant.

Marie: ⁴ _____ . I don't like spicy food.

Chris: Well, all right. ⁵ _____ trying that new Spanish restaurant?

Andy: ⁷ _____ ! I love it!

Chris: ⁸ _____ ?

Andy: Yes, I want to try the food there.

Marie: Yeah, okay.

4 working life

* easy to do
** a bit harder
*** extra challenge

Vocabulary

Work and young people

1 Match the words 1–6 with a–f to make collocations.

1	child	a	work
2	working	b	paid
3	earn	c	labour
4	career	d	conditions
5	full-time	e	your living
6	well	f	opportunities

2 Complete the text with the words below.

> career   conditions   educate   hours
> labour   living   treated   wages
> wealthy ✓   work

STOP CHILD LABOUR

If you're sixteen or seventeen and live in a ¹ _wealthy_ European country, you probably haven't started full-time ² _____ yet. Perhaps you work at weekends or in the holidays to earn some extra money, or to get experience which will improve your ³ _____ opportunities in the future. If you do, you are probably reasonably well ⁴ _____ ; and you can give up the job if you feel it doesn't leave you time to study for exams.

But in poor countries, child ⁵ _____ is part of everyday reality. Many parents cannot afford to ⁶ _____ their children. Children as young as seven or eight work to earn their ⁷ _____ . There are about 160 million child workers worldwide, often working long ⁸ _____ and always for very low ⁹ _____ .The working ¹⁰ _____ for them can be extremely unhealthy.

12 June 2011 is World Day Against Child Labour

Check our website to see what *you* can do!

Grammar

Obligation

3 (*) Match the sentences 1–5 with the signs a–e.

a    b   c

d **SILENCE**

e **Free entry**

1 You have to fasten your seat belts. `c`
2 You must be quiet. ☐
3 You don't have to pay to come in. ☐
4 You're not allowed to turn left. ☐
5 You mustn't cycle here. ☐

4 (**) Read the signs and notices below and complete the sentences with *must/mustn't, (don't) have to* or *are not allowed*. In one sentence there are two possible answers.

1 You _are not allowed_ to skateboard on the steps.

> **NO** SKATEBOARDING ON THESE STEPS

2 You _____ wear a uniform on Friday.

> Friday October 16th:
> NON-UNIFORM DAY

3 You _____ bring food or drink into the computer lab.

> NO FOOD OR DRINKS IN THE COMPUTER LAB !!!

4 You _____ slow down.

> REDUCE SPEED NOW

5 (✳✳✳) **Complete the dialogue between Millie and her grandma with the correct form (present or past) of** *(don't) have to, must, mustn't* **or** *be (not) allowed.*

Millie: Oh, Grandma. I'm so fed up with school. I ^{1} _have to_ wear this awful uniform. I ^{2} _____ to use my mobile phone at all during the day. I ^{3} _____ do about a million pages of homework every night, and Miss Grant always says 'You ^{4} _____ try harder! You ^{5} _____ forget about your exams!

Grandma: I'm sorry you're so tired, dear. But you ^{6} _____ study so hard tonight; it's Friday!

Millie: ^{7} _____ you _____ work this hard at school, Grandma?

Grandma: Let's see … we ^{8} _____ study Latin and that was quite difficult. On the other hand, we ^{9} _____ learn IT, because it didn't exist! And girls ^{10} _____ to do a lot of sports as people believed it wasn't necessary for us … but I don't think that was a good thing! We ^{11} _____ wear a full uniform, of course, and we ^{12} _____ to wear any jewellery.

Millie: Grandma, you ^{13} _____ write the story of your school days for us!

Grammar plus: *have got to* or *must (not)*

6 (✳✳✳) **Complete the sentences with the correct form of** *have got to* **or** *must (not).*

1 All employees _must_ wash their hands before returning to work.

2 'No, I can't come out tonight. I _____ help my brother with his project.'

3 Students _____ wear the school tie at all times.

4 Employees _____ use the company electronic communications system to send personal emails.

5 'I can't talk any longer. I _____ go.'

6 Visitors to the laboratory _____ touch the equipment.

Grammar reference

Obligation (*have to, must, don't have to, not allowed to, mustn't*)

Use of *have to* and *must*

• We use *have to* + verb to say that something is necessary (rules or laws):

*We **have to leave** our coats in the cloakroom.* (these are the rules)

In informal, spoken English we often use *have got to*:

*I'm sorry but I**'ve got to go** now.*

• We use *must* + verb to say that the speaker thinks something is necessary or important:

*I **must call** her as soon as I get home.* (it's important that I phone her)

*I **must talk** to my mother before making a decision.* (I'd really like to do that)

Must is often used to give strong advice or recommendations or to say that something is necessary in formal, written English:

*You **must** work harder if you want to pass the exam.* (strong recommendation)

*All passengers **must have** a passport valid for at least six months after the date of return to the UK.* (formal, written English)

The past form of both *must* and *have to* is *had to*:

*I didn't come because I **had to finish** my essay.*

Use of *don't have to*

• We use *don't have to* + verb to say that something is not necessary:

*We **don't have to wear** a school uniform.*

The past form of *don't have to* is *didn't have to*:

*When I was a child, I **didn't have to make** my bed.*

Use of *mustn't* and *not allowed to*

• We use *mustn't* + verb to say that something is not permitted or give strong advice/recommendations:

*You **mustn't park** here.* (it's not permitted)

*You **mustn't smoke** when you're pregnant.* (strong advice/recommendation)

• *Must not* is often used to say that things are forbidden in formal, written English:

*Passengers are reminded that luggage **must not** be left unattended at any time.*

• We use *not allowed to* + verb to say that something is not permitted and to give rules:

*My son **isn't allowed to watch** TV before he does his homework.* (it's the rule in our house)

The past form of *not allowed to* is *wasn't/weren't allowed to*:

*When I was a teenager, I **wasn't allowed to drink** coffee.*

Vocabulary

Jobs

1 Match the jobs 1–6 with the descriptions a–f.

1 A miner ——— a answers phone calls all day long.
2 A farm labourer b catches fish.
3 A governess → c works underground.
4 A servant d taught other people's children.
5 A call-centre worker e works in the fields.
6 A fisherman f did housework in another
person's home.

2 (**) Complete the sentences with the jobs from the box.

[PR consultant   advertising executive ✓   social worker
systems analyst]

1 Monica is an _advertising executive_ . She organises all
the work necessary to create an advertising campaign for
a company.
2 Paul is a _____ . He plans and sets up complex
computer systems for companies.
3 Tim is a _____ . He helps large companies
present a positive image of what they do.
4 Jenny is a _____ . She helps families with
problems.

3 Complete the interview with the words from the box.

[badly paid   challenging   employer   fun
repetitive ✓   respectable   stressful   supervisors]

Grammar

Make and let

4 (*) Read the sentences and
replace the parts in bold with the
phrases from the box.

[I have to   I'm allowed to ✓
I'm allowed to   I don't have to
I'm not allowed to]

1 **My parents let me** stay out late at
weekends.

I'm allowed to stay out
late at weekends.

2 But **they always make me** plan
who's bringing me back home
and when.

_____
_____

3 Fortunately, **they don't make me**
do my homework on Saturday
morning any longer.

_____
_____

4 **They let me** organise my own
study time.

_____
_____

5 But **they don't let me** stay up all
night in front of the computer.

_____
_____

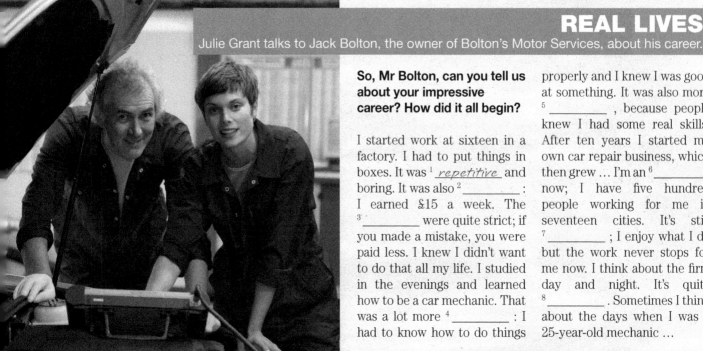

ADVERTISER   28 March

REAL LIVES

Julie Grant talks to Jack Bolton, the owner of Bolton's Motor Services, about his career.

**So, Mr Bolton, can you tell us
about your impressive
career? How did it all begin?**

I started work at sixteen in a
factory. I had to put things in
boxes. It was ¹ _repetitive_ and
boring. It was also ² _____ :
I earned £15 a week. The
³ _____ were quite strict; if
you made a mistake, you were
paid less. I knew I didn't want
to do that all my life. I studied
in the evenings and learned
how to be a car mechanic. That
was a lot more ⁴ _____ : I
had to know how to do things

properly and I knew I was good
at something. It was also more
⁵ _____ , because people
knew I had some real skills.
After ten years I started my
own car repair business, which
then grew ... I'm an ⁶ _____
now; I have five hundred
people working for me in
seventeen cities. It's still
⁷ _____ ; I enjoy what I do
but the work never stops for
me now. I think about the firm
day and night. It's quite
⁸ _____ . Sometimes I think
about the days when I was a
25-year-old mechanic ...

5 (**) Complete the text below with the correct form (present or past, positive or negative) of *make* or *let*.

My first memories of school are not very good. On the first day, the teacher
¹ _made_ *me sit next to a girl. The other boys laughed at me. The girl, Molly,*
didn't like it either; she never talked to me and she ² _____ *me use her*
pencil when I broke mine. She drew a line down the middle of the desk and
³ _____ *me keep to my side. But slowly we became friends. By the end*
of the year she ⁴ _____ *me touch her long red hair!*

My little son goes to an alternative school, where everything's different.
His teacher ⁵ _____ *the children sit with a different classmate every*
time, so that they all get to know each other. They have a lot of freedom
unlike traditional schools where the teacher ⁶ _____ *them stay in their*
chairs all the time. She ⁷ _____ *them stand up during the lesson to get*
the things they need: paper or colouring pencils and so on. In fact, I think
the only thing she ⁸ _____ *them do is hit other children!*

6 (**) Put the words in the correct order to make sentences.

1 him/~~Mike's~~/four/mum/go/week/to/cinema/the/times/lets/a
  Mike's _mum lets him go to the cinema four times a week_ .

2 music/parents/listen/let/don't/him/to/~~Luke's~~/loud
  Luke's _____ .

3 employer/lot/go/makes/of/her/~~Jane's~~/meetings/to/a
  Jane's _____ .

4 that/they/~~Fortunately~~/man/make/to/me/didn't/sit/next/boring
  Fortunately, _____ !

5 Ellen's/her/~~Last~~/an/parents/for the first time/to/let/Saturday/all-night party/go.
  Last _____ .

6 at lunchtime/employer/leave/let/~~Does~~/you/your/the office
  Does _____ ?

7 (***) Complete the second sentence so that it means the same as the first. Use *make* or *let*.

1 I only did it because they forced me to do it.
  I only did it because they _made me do_ it.

2 Most employers don't allow anyone to smoke in the office these days.
  Most employers _____ in the office these days.

3 Rainy weather always causes me to feel sleepy.
  Rainy weather always _____ sleepy.

4 My mother didn't force us to eat things we didn't like.
  My mother _____ things we didn't like.

5 My grandma's parents didn't allow her to go out with boys until she was eighteen!
  My grandma's parents didn't _____ out with boys until she was eighteen!

6 Did they force you to pay for the broken cup at the café?
  Did they _____ for the broken cup at the café?

Grammar reference

make and *let*

Sometimes two verbs follow one another in a sentence. The second verb can take a different form, depending on the first verb. After *make* and *let*, the second verb follows the pattern: object + infinitive without *to*.

make

make + object + infinitive without *to* means to force someone to do something:

*My mother **makes me clean** my bedroom every Saturday.*
(= she forces me to clean my bedroom – I have to do it)

*I was so happy that our parents **didn't make us apologise** to the neighbour.*
(= our parents didn't force us to apologise – we didn't have to do it)

let

let + object + infinitive without *to* means to allow someone to do something:

*My grandmother always **lets me eat** sweets after dinner.*
(= she allows me to eat sweets – I can do it)

*The teacher **didn't let us leave** the classroom before the end of the test.*
(= the teacher didn't allow us to leave the classroom – we couldn't do it)

Vocabulary

Making a living

1 Complete the sentences with the correct form of the words in brackets.

1 Money is less important to me than being happy with my job. I want my job to be _rewarding_ (reward).

2 Mark hasn't got a job at the moment, he's _____ (employ).

3 Jackie started a business a few years ago and it's been very _____ (succeed). Now she employs over a hundred people.

4 I think you should _____ (advertisement) your products on the internet.

5 In modern business, you have to _____ (reaction) to changes in technology and adapt.

2 Choose the best word, a, b or c to complete the gaps in the text.

STARTING WORK

So, you've finally finished all your exams and now you want to start work and ¹ _a_ some money. Everyone has to ² ____ a living by working, but you should choose a job that you will enjoy – after all, you will ³ ____ a lot of time doing it! Many companies ask you to ⁴ ____ some work experience before you start. If you can't find a job immediately, then don't ⁵ ____ your life waiting for the right job – volunteer somewhere. Melanie volunteered to help in an advertising agency and got some great experience there. Now she ⁶ ____ her living by doing the same thing. 'I started off making coffee for people and making photocopies, but now I ⁷ ____ my own business! I ⁸ ____ a lot of money, but more importantly, I love my job,' she explains.

1 **a** earn ✓	**b** take	**c** waste
2 **a** get	**b** do	**c** make
3 **a** pass	**b** spend	**c** have
4 **a** try	**b** get	**c** make
5 **a** waste	**b** get	**c** pass
6 **a** works	**b** gets	**c** earns
7 **a** do	**b** run	**c** start
8 **a** make	**b** take	**c** run

Reading

3 Look at the texts A–C on page 33 and match them to the correct text type 1–3.

1 ☐ magazine interview

2 ☐ a newspaper article

3 ☐ website

4 Read text A about Ben Southall. Tick (✓) true or cross (✗) false or write (?) if there is no information.

1 ☐ Ben Southall is Australian.

2 ☐ The sixteen finalists enjoyed their four-day stay on the island.

3 ☐ They announced that Southall got the job on a TV programme.

4 ☐ Southall has to write a blog every day about life on the island.

5 ☐ The living conditions for the job are not very good.

5 Read texts B and C and choose the correct answers.

1 Which is true about Mike's job?
   a Mike doesn't want to work full-time.
   b Mike would prefer to work as a computer operator.
   c Mike doesn't like working with primary school children.
   d In his job, Mike has to wear special clothes and travel.

2 Jane
   a works as a DVD tester now.
   b worked as a DVD tester for a long time.
   c liked working as a DVD tester.
   d thought the job wasn't very easy.

3 What is true about Michelle's job?
   a It isn't easy to prepare the food when the boat is at sea.
   b You don't need any special skills to do it.
   c She only ever works part-time, not full-time.
   d She thinks travelling in bad weather is exciting.

6 Read all the texts again and answer the questions.

1 How much will Southall earn?

_____

2 When did Mike start his job?

_____

3 What was difficult about Jane's job?

_____

4 Did Jane see any good films?

_____

5 How long has Michelle had her job?

_____

6 Why does she like her job?

_____

British man gets world's 'best job'!

A British man has beaten more than 34,000 applicants to get the position described as 'the best job in the world'.

Ben Southall, 34, was chosen from sixteen finalists after spending four days on Hamilton Island, in Australia's Great Barrier Reef. The finalists had to show their swimming and snorkelling abilities and their blog-writing skills. Tourism Queensland announced that Southall was the successful candidate in a reality TV show.

Southall's job description? 'To explore the islands of the Great Barrier Reef, swim, snorkel, make friends with the local people and generally enjoy the tropical climate and lifestyle.' Southall also has to write a daily blog on the website and make a photo diary and videos as well as interviewing tourists and local people. For his island job, he'll earn £73,500, and live in a three-bedroomed house with a swimming pool.

---

http://thejobforum.co.uk

The Job Forum

Forum | Vacancies | Blogs

Have you got an unusual or interesting job? What's the strangest job you've ever done? Write and tell us!

Henry VIII re-enactor

For the past eighteen months I've had a full-time job as a Henry VIII re-enactor! I dress up as King Henry VIII and visit primary schools around the country to bring history to life. I try to help children imagine what life was like in 1509 when Henry became King of England. It's great fun and much better than my old job as a computer operator!

Mike, Crewe

DVD tester

Last summer I worked as a DVD tester. I had to watch the DVDs and check they worked OK. I love films so it was a fantastic job – and it was very easy. The only problem was that I worked at night and it was hard not to fall asleep because I was often tired. In the morning I often couldn't remember all the films I watched! I had to watch some terrible films, but I saw lots of good ones too.

Jane, Aberdeen

Ⓒ

This week in *Jobs Today* we talk to Michelle Bush, who is a cook on a yacht.

JT: Michelle, when did you start the job?
MB: Seven years ago.
JT: What skills do you need?
MB: You need to be a good cook, friendly and hard-working. It helps if you have good people skills, too. If you get seasick, this is not the job for you. It's difficult to prepare and cook food in a very small space when the boat is moving!
JT: What hours do you work?
MB: You can work part-time, but I often work fourteen hours a day, with no weekends off.
JT: What's the best part of the job?
MB: I meet some interesting people and I travel to a lot of exotic places.
JT: And the worst part?
MB: When the weather is bad, being on the yacht at sea is frightening. I don't like that.

Reading

Multiple matching

1 Read about Josh's first girlfriend, Ava. Underline what he says about the following things, as in the example.

- Ava's appearance
- Ava's personality
- how the relationship ended

3 Read three people's descriptions of their first girlfriend/boyfriend. Match the statements 1–7 below to the people A–C. You can choose each person more than once.

Internet Forum

Share your memories of your first boyfriend or girlfriend. Click [here] to add a post.

Josh

When Ava agreed to go out with me, I thought I was the luckiest guy in the world. She looked like a fashion model; beautiful and glamorous. She was taller than me, actually! I didn't understand what she saw in an ordinary guy like me. She was very sociable and loved going out … and being the centre of attention. She loved talking about herself and about her shopping – she could do that for hours. But when I tried to tell her something, she stopped listening very quickly. In the end, I decided to find myself a girlfriend I could talk to for a change!

Internet Forum

A Ann

My first boyfriend Charlie and I were in the same class in secondary school. I liked him from the beginning; he had red wavy hair and a funny round face with freckles. When we were eleven, he was small and plump, but then in two years he grew tall and thin and looked really cool. He was easy-going, friendly and great fun to be with … and he still is. He was a great boyfriend and now he's a great husband!

B Alice

Adam was good-looking, with lots of dark wavy hair, but his clothes often looked a bit scruffy. That was because he often climbed trees and got into strange places to photograph birds. He was really into photography. He always had a camera with him and took pictures of people, houses, trees, of everything really … and also of me. He's a professional photographer now, and when I see his work in a book or magazine I sometimes think, 'I was in his earliest photos.'

C Matt

My first girlfriend was Amy in primary school. We were both seven years old. She had lovely grey eyes and long, soft hair, and I told her she was almost as beautiful as my mum. She was a very good girlfriend: she always gave me one of her sandwiches. I gave her my favourite model car, a red Porsche, and we promised to get married in the future. I was very jealous when she talked to other boys, but I said nothing, because my dad told me a man must respect a woman's freedom.

2 Read the five sentences below. Tick (✓) the ones that are true about Ava and her relationship with Josh.

1 She was perfect in every way.

2 Her personality was less attractive than her appearance.

3 She left me because I wasn't glamorous.

4 I decided she was not the right person for me.

5 She was talkative and self-centred.

Which person says this about his/her first boyfriend/girlfriend?

1 ☐ His/Her appearance changed with age.

2 ☐ He/She shared something with me.

3 ☐ I compared him/her to someone I admired.

4 ☐ We eventually got married.

5 ☐ He/She had an artistic passion.

6 ☐ We met at a very early age.

7 ☐ He/She was attractive but didn't look tidy.

Listening

True/False/No information

4 Read these pairs of sentences. Tick (✓) if they mean the same, cross (✗) if they don't.

- ☐ 1 a He often works long hours.
    b He always works long hours.
- ☐ 2 a This job is never stressful.
    b If you learn to relax, this job is not stressful.
- ☐ 3 a She did badly paid work all her life.
    b She was never well paid.
- ☐ 4 a Some of my customers are polite.
    b All of my customers are polite.
- ☐ 5 a It's always exciting.
    b It's exciting every time.

Exam TIP

When deciding whether a statement says the same as the text, pay attention to words such as *always*, *every time*, *often*, *never*, *all*, *some*. Some of them mean the same, but others don't.

5 (7) Listen to an interview with a hairdresser. Read the three statements below. Listen to the first part of the interview as many times as you need to. Match the statements 1–3 with the answers a–c and complete the explanations.

1 ☐ Rita enjoys working with people.
2 ☐ Rita thinks a hairdresser's work is always creative and challenging.
3 ☐ Every person's hair changes with age.

a The statement is *false* because Rita says 'If you _____ , it's _____ !'

b There is *no information* because she talks about something else. She says 'The same _____ is different at different _____ .'

c The statement is *true* because she says 'It's _____ because I work _____ .'

6 (8) Listen to the second part of the interview twice. Tick (✓) true or cross (✗) false. If there is *no information* in the recording, write (?).

1 ☐ I have never damaged a customer's hair.
2 ☐ Customers always expect good work.
3 ☐ Before New Year's Eve customers ask for special party hairstyles.
4 ☐ I chat with all my customers.
5 ☐ The business executive always falls asleep.
6 ☐ Some customers talk about their families.
7 ☐ Some customers say they'd like to be fashion models.

Use of English

Word formation

7 Look at the examples of adjectives formed with suffixes. Build adjectives from the words from the box using the same suffixes.

> talk   stress   rely   boss   ambition ✓

1 glamour – glamor**ous**   *ambition* – *ambitious*
2 respect – respect**able**   _____ – _____
3 wealth – wealth**y**   _____ – _____
4 repeat – repet**itive**   _____ – _____
5 beauty – beauti**ful**   _____ – _____

8 Make the adjectives from the box negative by adding the prefixes *un-* or *in-*.

> ambitious ✓   decisive   formal   happy
> sensitive   successful   tidy

un-: *unambitious* _____
_____   _____

in-: _____   _____
_____

Exam TIP

Learn the different prefixes and suffixes used to build new words. Always think about the meaning of the gapped sentence before you put in the missing word. Does it need a negative prefix – especially when it is an adjective?

9 Use the words in brackets to build words to complete the text.

The unusual twins

Julia and Lucy are twin sisters, but they are
[1] *completely* (complete) different. Julia is extremely [2] _____ (ambition). To her, the most important thing is to have a [3] _____ (respect) job with a large company. She thinks there's nothing worse than being [4] _____ (success). Lucy is not interested in a career in business. She says it's much too [5] _____ (stress) and would make her [6] _____ (happy). Lucy enjoys making [7] _____ (beauty) things, but she's not sure what she wants to do. Her aunts ask her 'Don't you want to achieve anything? You're so [8] _____ (decide)!' But Lucy just laughs and says 'Perhaps I'll just marry a [9] _____ (wealth) man … !'

self-assessment test 2

Vocabulary & Grammar

1 Choose the best word a, b or c to complete the sentences.

1 I'd hate to be _b_ . I can't stand talking on the phone.
   a a system analyst   b a call-centre worker ✓
   c an advertising executive

2 He earns a lot of money – his job is very ___ .
   a well-treated   b wealthy   c well-paid

3 My father is going ___ . He hasn't got much hair.
   a bald   b plump   c scruffy

4 I'm quite ambitious so career ___ are important to me.
   a opportunities   b supervisors
   c conditions

5 Robert is ___ . He'll be fifteen tomorrow.
   a in his fifties   b middle-aged
   c in his teens

6 My sister is very ___ . She always tells me what to do.
   a self-centred   b bossy   c organised

7 Jessica's hair is not wavy, it's ___ .
   a dark   b straight   c medium-length

/6

2 Complete the sentences with the correct form of the adjectives from the box. Add any necessary words.

> indecisive   nice   argumentative
> organised   beautiful ✓   sociable

1 In my opinion, Julia Roberts is _more beautiful than_ Angelina Jolie.

2 Don't you know what time your appointment is tomorrow? Why can't you be a little _____ , Sara?

3 Mrs Perkins is _____ neighbour on our street. She's always ready to help.

4 My boyfriend's _____ me. I don't like going to parties so much.

5 Peter is _____ Tom. They both argue a lot.

6 Jill never knows what to choose in a shop. She's _____ person I know.

/5

3 Complete the sentences with one letter in each gap.

1 Olivia gets upset very easily. She's very
   s _e_n_s_i_t_i_v_e_ .

2 My job is very boring and r _ _ _ _ _ _ _ _ .
   I do the same things every day.

3 A s _ _ _ _ _ worker works with children and families who need help.

4 I'm sorry but I can't accept f _ _ _ _ _ _ _ work.
   I can work only three days a week.

5 What a pretty dress! You look very
   g _ _ _ _ _ _ _ _ in it, Sylvia.

6 Sam doesn't like his job, but he works hard because he needs to earn his l _ _ _ _ _ .

7 My sister is really s _ _ . She never talks to anybody and is not very confident.

/6

4 Underline the correct words to complete the sentences.

1 Your jacket looks very similar *as/to* mine.

2 At your age, I *had to/must* make my bed myself.

3 Let me *go/to go*, Mum! I'll be back by ten.

4 My brother's *much/more* older than Nick.

5 We *mustn't/don't have to* go to school tomorrow. It's Sunday.

6 The film was different *of/from* the book.

7 My English teacher makes us *to read/read* a lot.

8 The rules in my school are very strict – you're *not allowed/don't have* to use your mobile.

9 I think Bethany is *as/less* clever as Hannah.

/8

5 Complete the gaps in the text with the correct form of the words in brackets.

LOOKING FOR A SUMMER JOB? We've got something for you! No job for this summer? We'll search our database for a perfect job for you. Hundreds of [1] _employers_ (employ) are looking for someone with your skills now. Our summer jobs are fun but also [2] _____ (challenge), so you can learn new things. Some positions can be quite [3] _____ (stress) – that's why we're looking for people with a strong [4] _____ (person).

If you're hard-working and [5] _____ (ambition) – call us now! We'll find a [6] _____ (reward) job for you.

/5

36

Reading

6 Read four teenagers' texts from the school newsletter. Answer the questions below with their names (David, Rebecca, Paul, Olivia).

How did you earn your first money?

David:
When I was fifteen I was desperate to earn some money, so I decided to do a paper round before school. I started at six every morning, and did it all on foot. I'm not a good cyclist, especially with a heavy load of newspapers. The pay was not good but still better than my pocket money! On the whole, it was a good experience, but a bit boring. I had to do the same thing every day. My mother was not happy because I was very tired and my marks at school got worse. She let me do it for only six months.

Rebecca:
I earned my first money babysitting for our neighbour. I was almost fifteen and quite responsible. One night my neighbour wanted to go out with some friends and asked me to stay with her daughter, Lucy, for a couple of hours. Lucy was four and knew me quite well. But the moment her mum left, she started screaming and wouldn't stop. I tried phoning her mum, but couldn't get through. I didn't know what to do. Those were the longest two hours of my life! And, of course, Lucy stopped crying the minute her mum walked through the door!

Paul:
I earned my first money by walking dogs. Dog walking sounds like fun but it can also be challenging if you have to walk several dogs a day. In my first job I walked seven dogs, collecting them from different places at different times each day. It was easy to make a mistake, so every evening I wrote down all the addresses, the dogs' names and the exact time I was walking them the next day. I loved the experience and I'm definitely going to work with animals after I finish school.

Olivia:
When I finished primary school, I started earning money at home doing stuff like cleaning the car and digging the garden. My mother always said 'the money is there if you put in the time and effort'. The problem was that she made me do things I didn't like. And sometimes she wasn't really pleased with the results. Now I don't have time to earn money in this way – I'm too busy preparing for my A-levels.

Who:

1 was not very conscientious? _____

2 had to plan his/her work very carefully? _____

3 wasn't allowed to continue with his/her job? _____

4 has made a decision about his/her future career? _____

5 found his/her first job extremely stressful? _____

6 thought his/her job was badly-paid? _____

7 worked for his/her family? _____

8 found his/her first job repetitive? _____

/8

Communication

7 Complete the dialogues with the phrases from the box.

> what about ✓   think of
> another idea   've got
> 'm not sure   how about   all right
> don't think   all agree   not bad

1 Tom: ¹ _What about_ going to the cinema tonight, Ian?

Ian: I ² _____ about that. I've got Maths homework to do for tomorrow.

Tom: Okay. Here's ³ _____ . I'll help you with your Maths first and then we'll go.

Ian: Well, ⁴ _____ then. Thanks.

2 Mum: We need a name for our new puppy.

Julia: What do you ⁵ _____ Flossy?

Nick: It's ⁶ _____ but it sounds a bit like a cat's name.

Julia: A cat's name? Maybe you're right. I ⁷ _____ a better idea. ⁸ _____ Pluto?

Nick: That's it. I love it! And I ⁹ _____ anybody can say it's a cat's name.

Mum: Do we ¹⁰ _____ , then?

Julia, Nick: Yeah!

/9

8 Write questions for the given answers.

1 A: _____

B: She's very tall and slim.

2 A: _____

B: They like playing basketball.

3 A: _____

B: He's very easy-going.

/3

Marks

Vocabulary & Grammar	/30 marks
Reading	/8 marks
Communication	/12 marks
Total:	/50 marks

5 getting there

* easy to do
** a bit harder
*** extra challenge

Vocabulary

Protecting the environment

1 Match words 1–6 with a–f to make collocations.

1 save/waste
2 recycle
3 turn down/up
4 global
5 protect/destroy
6 reduce

a the heating
b warming
c the environment/wildlife
d pollution
e energy/fuel
f paper/glass/plastic

2 <u>Underline</u> the correct words to complete the sentences.

1 Look, there are lights on in all the rooms. We shouldn't <u>waste</u>/save energy like that.

2 It's so hot! Can you turn *down/up* the heating?

3 Please remember to switch *on/off* the light when you leave.

4 Don't throw *away/up* this paper. Recycle it.

5 Governments are working on ways of *reducing/protecting* carbon emissions.

6 Pollution from cars and planes is *destroying/saving* the environment.

3 Read the sentences. Tick (✓) the ones that are true and correct the ones that are false, using the words and phrases from the box.

> less   no animal products   save
> the amount of carbon dioxide we produce ✓

1 Carbon footprint is ~~the name of a common gas.~~
   the amount of carbon dioxide we produce.

2 A vegan is a person who eats fruit, vegetables and milk products.
   _____

3 Global warming is probably caused by carbon dioxide emissions.
   _____

4 Energy-saving light bulbs help us waste energy.
   _____

5 If you recycle paper, glass and plastic, you throw away more.
   _____

6 Turning down the heating is one of the ways in which we can protect the environment.
   _____

Grammar

Future with *will* and *going to*

4 (*) Look at the pictures and write sentences with *going to* using the verbs and phrases from the box.

> fall   jump   recycle their waste
> learn to ride a bike ✓   be a storm

1 He *'s going to learn to ride a bike* .
2 She _____ .
3 They _____ .
4 There _____ .
5 He _____ .

5 (*) Complete the sentences with *will* or *won't*.

1 Do you believe our new recycling bins *will* make a difference to the environment?

2 Don't worry. I'm sure you _____ fail. You've practised so hard.

3 What time do you think they _____ arrive?

4 I'm sure she _____ like Tom; he's such a nice guy.

5 I hope the new road _____ destroy local wildlife.

6 (✷✷) **Complete the dialogue with *going to* and the verbs from the box.**

invite   make   spend   wear   have   get ✓

Jo: Guess what? Chris and I are getting married.

Sue: Congratulations. That's fantastic! When ¹ *are you going to get* married?

Jo: In June.

Sue: And who ² _____ ?

Jo: We're ³ _____ a very quiet wedding, so just a couple of friends. You, for example!

Sue: What ⁴ _____ ?

Jo: Just a simple white dress.

Sue: And who ⁵ _____ a speech?

Jo: Chris's brother, I think.

Sue: And where ⁶ _____ your honeymoon?

Jo: In the Lake District.

7 (✷✷) **Complete the sentences with *will* or *going to* and the verbs in brackets.**

1 I *'m going to wash* (wash) the car today. I've wanted to do it for weeks.

2 She belongs to a group that believes the world _____ (end) in 2034.

3 Look at these clouds. It _____ (rain).

4 I'm optimistic: I think people _____ (learn) to protect the environment better in the future.

5 I know they _____ (not/help) us. We'll have to manage by ourselves.

6 What _____ (you/do) with your old laptop? Could I have it?

Grammar reference

Future with *will* and *going to*

Use of *going to*

- We use *going to* + infinitive to talk about intentions and plans:

*Next year **I'm going to give up** smoking.*
*He **is going to visit** his grandmother at the weekend.*

- We use *going to* + infinitive to make predictions based on evidence or something we can see now:

*I think they**'re going to lose**.* (The score is 0:3 at the moment and they are playing very badly)
*Look at that girl! She**'s going to fall off** her horse!* (I can see that the horse has tripped over a stone)

Use of *will*

- We use *will/won't* + infinitive without *to* to make predictions based on what we think or believe, or on experience:

*I'm quite sure you **will like** this film.* (prediction based on my belief)
*I think she**'ll fail** her driving test again.* (prediction based on experience – she's already failed her driving test once)

- We often start predictions with *will* with phrases like:

*I think (that) … I believe (that) …
I'm sure (that) …*

Vocabulary

Transport and the environment

1 Match the words 1–5 with a–e to make collocations.

1 public — a licence
2 bus — b jam
3 driver's — c lane
4 cycle → d transport
5 traffic — e pass

2 Complete the texts with the words below.

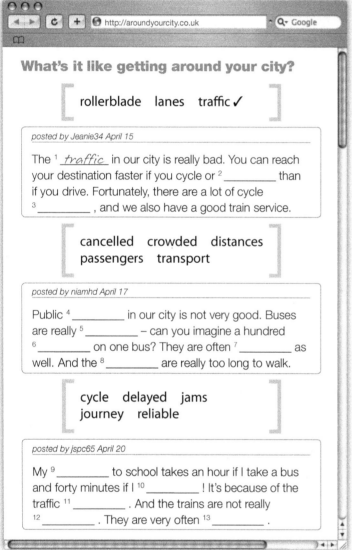

http://aroundyourcity.co.uk   Google

What's it like getting around your city?

[rollerblade   lanes   traffic ✓]

posted by Jeanie34 April 15

The ¹ _traffic_ in our city is really bad. You can reach your destination faster if you cycle or ² _____ than if you drive. Fortunately, there are a lot of cycle ³ _____ , and we also have a good train service.

[cancelled   crowded   distances
passengers   transport]

posted by niamhd April 17

Public ⁴ _____ in our city is not very good. Buses are really ⁵ _____ – can you imagine a hundred ⁶ _____ on one bus? They are often ⁷ _____ as well. And the ⁸ _____ are really too long to walk.

[cycle   delayed   jams
journey   reliable]

posted by jspc65 April 20

My ⁹ _____ to school takes an hour if I take a bus and forty minutes if I ¹⁰ _____ ! It's because of the traffic ¹¹ _____ . And the trains are not really ¹² _____ . They are very often ¹³ _____ .

3 **Underline** the correct preposition to complete each multi-word verb in the sentences.

1 I was lucky: I got *on*/*off* the bus just before it started to rain.

2 Jane felt ill at school, so her dad picked her *off*/*up*.

3 Sam gets *on*/*around* the city on his bike most of the time.

4 When I go *out*/*up* in the morning, I see a huge traffic jam all along our street.

5 The girl got *off*/*out* the train at the wrong station.

Grammar

First conditional and future time clauses

4 **a** ✱ Match the sentence beginnings 1–6 with the endings a–f.

1 If I become president,
2 He'll be sick,
3 If you clean the floor,
4 You'll break it,
5 I'll be home at five,
6 If you leave the letter on the table,

a if you aren't careful.
b unless there's another meeting.
c I'll protect the environment.
d if he eats all those chocolates.
e I'll post it for you.
f I'll do the washing up.

b **Match the sentences from exercise 4a to the pictures.**

5

(**) Complete the sentences with the verbs in brackets in the correct form for future situations.

1 I _'ll let_ (let) you have this book as soon as I _finish_ (finish) it.

2 When Mum _____ (see) what we've done, she _____ (be) very angry.

3 I _____ (ask) him to phone you as soon as he _____ (come) back.

4 I _____ (not let) you go until you _____ (tell) me the truth.

5 If we _____ (be) late, they _____ (start) without us.

6

(***) Complete the second sentence so that it means the same as the first. Use *unless*.

1 If you don't hurry up, we'll be late. Unless _you hurry up_ , we'll be late.

2 He won't pass the driving test if he doesn't learn how to park. He won't pass the driving test _____ how to park.

3 If the weather doesn't change, we'll go to the mountains next week. We'll go to the mountains next week unless _____ .

4 I won't finish this work on time if you don't help me. I won't finish this work on time _____ me.

5 I'll call the police if they don't stop that noise. I'll call the police unless _____ .

Grammar plus: *in case* + present simple

7

(***) Complete the second sentence with *in case* and the idea from the first sentence.

1 We might see something we want to buy. Take some money _in case we see_ something we want to buy.

2 My flight may be delayed. I always travel with a book _____ delayed.

3 Someone might come. Let's buy more food _____ .

4 Bill might call. I don't want to go out _____ .

5 You might lose your suitcase. Write your name and address on your suitcase _____ it.

6 I might not see you before I leave. I'll say goodbye now _____ before I leave.

Grammar reference

First conditional and future time clauses

First conditional

- We use the first conditional to talk about possible future situations. But after *if* we use the present tense, not the future.

Form

Condition	Result
if + present simple	*will/won't* + infinitive without *to*
If you **come** fifteen minutes before the class starts,	I'**ll help** you with your homework.
If the weather **is** fine,	we'**ll go** swimming.
If Sam **passes** his exams,	his parents **will buy** him a car.
If Alice **doesn't eat** her vegetables,	she **won't get** any sweets.

- *If* can go at the beginning or in the middle of the sentence. When we put the *if* clause first, we use a comma (,) to separate the two clauses:

If I see him, I'll pass on the message.

- When we put the main clause first, we don't use a comma:

I'll pass on the message **if** I see him.

- In conditional sentences, we can use *unless* (= if not) instead of *if*.

Her father **won't let** her go out **unless** she **does** her homework for tomorrow. (Her father won't let her go out if she doesn't do her homework for tomorrow.)
I'**ll tell** Robert everything **unless** you **want** me to keep a secret.

Future time clauses

- We also use the present simple to talk about the future after these time expressions *when, after, before, as soon as, until*:

I'**ll take** a gap year **when** I **finish** school.
She'**ll need** a lot of rest **after** she **comes** back from hospital.
We'**ll get** in touch **before** we **make** plans to visit your city.
I'**ll text** you **as soon as** our plane **lands**.
I **will continue** taking driving lessons **until** I **feel** confident I can pass the test.

In case + present simple

- *In case* + present simple means 'because something might happen'. We use it to talk about things/ situations we usually want to avoid. The main clause is *will* + infinitive without *to* or imperative:

I'**ll take** the umbrella with me **in case** it **rains**.
(I'll take the umbrella with me because it might rain; I'd like to avoid getting wet.)
I'**ll check** the computer before my presentation **in case** it **doesn't work**.
Say hello to your cousin from me **in case** I **don't see** him again.
Take the house keys with you **in case** you **get** home before me.

Vocabulary

Travel and eco-tourism

1 Match words 1–7 with a–g to make compound nouns.

1	travel	**a**	guide
2	luxury	**b**	company
3	holiday	**c**	correspondent
4	tourist	**d**	animals
5	tropical	**e**	work
6	endangered	**f**	holiday
7	voluntary	**g**	forest

2 Complete the sentences using the compound nouns from exercise 1.

1 Jane is a ¹ *travel correspondent* for a magazine. This month, she's travelling to India and writing about ² _____ .

2 I don't want to spend lots of money on a ³ _____ . I want to help people so I usually do some ⁴ _____ .

3 The ⁵ _____ told the visitors all about the history of the castle.

4 We went to the Amazon to visit a ⁶ _____ and see the wildlife.

5 Which ⁷ _____ did you use to book your holiday?

3 Complete the magazine article with the words below. There are two extra words.

> sightseeing   villa   luxury   ship
> caravans   exotic ✓   balloon   tickets
> lands   passengers   remote   tours   visit

Holiday Cool

Summer is coming, so what are the coolest holidays this year? Read our tips and find out!

The Bahamas

These ¹ *exotic* islands are the perfect location for a ² _____ holiday. Stay in a ³ _____ instead of a hotel.

Greece

It's the coolest place to visit ancient monuments and beautiful islands. There are lots of well-organised ⁴ _____ and plenty of opportunities for ⁵ _____ .

Cruises

A cruise ⁶ _____ is a great way to travel if you love the sea! You sleep and eat on the boat, but you stop at various places too. You can soon meet all the other ⁷ _____ and have lots of fun. Remember, ⁸ _____ sell out fast, so book early.

Listening

4 You are going to listen to five street interviews. Read the interviewer's questions below and tick (✓) the words you think you will probably hear in the text.

- Who do you think should be responsible for reducing carbon emissions? Individuals or the government?
- What do you personally do to save energy?

☐ pollution   ☐ relationships
☐ public transport   ☐ cars
☐ shopping

5 ⑨ Read the opinions a–g. Then listen to the interviews and match the speakers 1–5 with their opinions a–g. There are two extra opinions.

1	☐ Sally	4	☐ Mark
2	☐ Ben	5	☐ Alex
3	☐ Kathy		

a thinks public transport in his/her area is very bad.

b thinks there should be more laws to cut down on pollution.

c thinks it's important to recycle domestic rubbish.

d thinks it's better to walk than take public transport.

e says people create more pollution than industry.

f thinks it's better to cycle to reduce traffic jams.

g says it's better not to buy new things very often.

6 ⑨ Listen to the interviews again and choose the correct answers.

1 Sally thinks that
   a better public transport would reduce traffic jams.
   b public transport uses a lot of fuel.
   c there are enough buses and trains already.
   d it's easier to drive everywhere than take the bus.

2 Ben
   a only drives to go to the shops, not to work.
   b uses his car to get to work.
   c doesn't like using public transport.
   d drives and uses public transport.

3 Mark says that
   a he usually walks home from school.
   b he travels home by bike now instead of by car.
   c his mum picks him up from school every day.
   d he uses public transport to travel home from school.

Reading

7 Read the introduction to the interview and choose the best answer.

The text is about

a what a typical teenager can do to protect the environment.

b a family that tries to be environmentally-friendly.

8 Read the interview and match the missing phrases and sentences a–f to the correct place 1–6 in the text.

a We went on a trip in a hot-air balloon last month!

b Well, we did all the usual things,

c Well, first I persuaded my parents

d I looked on the internet to find out where electricity comes from.

e No, there's loads to do!

f I broke my promise a lot, so I tried something else.

9 Read the interview again. Tick (✓) true or cross (✗) false or write (?) if there is no information.

1 ☐ Electricity in Britain is very expensive.

2 ☐ All the members of Connal's family talked about ways to use less energy.

3 ☐ Each family member promised to do one thing every month to save energy.

4 ☐ Using the computer for an hour less every day saves a lot of energy.

5 ☐ Connal had to get up much earlier to cycle to school.

6 ☐ Next month, members of the family will only use one gadget, on Thursdays.

How to be eco-friendly

These days, everyone knows it's important to protect the environment and reduce their carbon footprint. But how often have you said *What I do doesn't make a difference*? If everyone makes excuses like this, then no positive changes happen. Stuck for ideas about what to do? Read about Connal Barry and his family – they've had some great ideas!

EcoLife: First of all, why did you decide to become more eco-friendly?

Connal: Well, my dad was always telling me to turn off the TV or computer – he complained about the cost of electricity! He kept saying it wasn't good for the planet, either. ¹ ___ That's when I realised that most energy sources are running out.

EcoLife: What did you do?

Connal: ² ___ to change their electricity supplier to a green supplier. Then the whole family – me, my parents, and my sister, Sarah – sat down to discuss what we could do at home to save energy.

EcoLife: And?

Connal: ³ ___ like not leaving the computer and TV on standby, using energy-saving light bulbs, turning the heating down and recycling more stuff … but then we decided that wasn't enough.

EcoLife: What else did you do?

Connal: We all promised to do one energy-saving thing every month.

EcoLife: What did you do?

Connal: Well, first I said I would use the computer for an hour less each day, but I love computer games and chatting online so that was really difficult! ⁴ ___ I got up just half an hour earlier during the week and cycled to school instead of taking the bus. I got much fitter and I didn't feel so bad about using the computer so much!

EcoLife: What about the rest of the family?

Connal: Last month, my dad used public transport to get to work, instead of driving. My mum switched her mobile off every afternoon – she found that difficult because she often texts her friends. My sister stopped using her hair-dryer.

EcoLife: And if everyone keeps their promise for a month, you do something fun together – is that right?

Connal: Yes. ⁵ ___ It was so cool.

EcoLife: And what's your next energy-saving idea?

Connal: Next month, we're going to have a gadget-free day every Thursday.

EcoLife: What's that?

Connal: We don't use any gadgets! You know, no computer, no TV, no mobile phone, no mp3 player, no CD player, no microwave …

EcoLife: That sounds difficult!

Connal: ⁶ ___ We're going to play board games – I'm learning chess. And we're having a homework-help hour – my parents will help us with any problems. Oh, and if the weather's good, we're going to have a barbecue in the garden!

Writing

A description of a place

1 In the **introduction**, give information about:
– the geographical location:
it's on the coast …
it's in the north/south/east/west/centre of the country …
it's near London …
– population:
the population is about …
with a population of …
– what kind of place it is:
a busy industrial city …
a small traditional village …

2 In **paragraph 2**, describe some of the famous sights:
some of the most famous landmarks are …
if you go sightseeing, you shouldn't miss the National Gallery …

Madrid

Madrid is the capital of Spain and the largest city, with a population of around 3.2 million. It is located on the river Manzanares in the centre of the country. As the capital city, it is an important political and business centre and a popular tourist destination.

Madrid is famous for its beautiful old buildings such as the Royal Palace, the Teatro Real (Royal Theatre) and the National Library. It also has three world-famous art museums, as well as many other interesting museums and galleries. There are many lovely parks to walk and relax in, such as the Retiro Park. Madrid is easy to get around because it has an extensive underground train network called the 'Metro'.

You should definitely visit the historic centre. You can sit and have a drink in the Plaza Mayor, a beautiful old square. The streets around the Plaza Mayor are narrow and they are always busy because there are many traditional cafés, restaurants and shops. If you like shopping, there is a huge street market every Sunday, called 'El Rastro'. You can buy anything there, from clothes to souvenirs, plants to jewellery.

Madrid is a wonderful city to visit and the people are very friendly. Perhaps the best time to visit is May, during the festival of San Isidro, the patron saint of Madrid. There are lots of free music concerts and fantastic fireworks – you'll have a great time if you come.

3 In **paragraph 3**, give more information ab the place, e.g. descr typical area or famo people who live/ha lived there. Try to us variety of adjectives *a beautiful square, b narrow streets, restaurants …*

4 In the **conclusion**, summarise what ma the place special, an recommend someth interesting to see or

1 Read the description of Madrid and answer the questions.

1 How many people live in Madrid? _____

2 What is the Retiro? _____

3 What can you buy in the street market?
_____

4 What happens during the festival of San Isidro?
_____

2 Find the adjectives below in the description in exercise 1. Put them in the right category.

popular   busy   huge   world-famous   lovely   friendly   important   interesting   easy to get around   beautiful ✓   narrow   historic   old   traditional   wonderful   fantastic   great

1 a town/city/area: *beautiful,* _____
2 buildings: *beautiful,* _____
3 people: _____
4 other places, e.g. parks, museums, markets
_____
5 transport: _____
6 general description: *beautiful,* _____

3 **a** Read Jo's notes for her introduction to a description of Berlin. Tick (✓) two things Jo needs to do to improve the introduction.

- Berlin is on the Spree River.
  The population is about 3.4 million.
- It is one of the most popular tourist destinations in Europe.
- It is in the east of the country. It is the capital city. It is a busy city.
- It is an important political, scientific and cultural centre. It is the largest city in Germany.

1 ☐ Organise the information.
2 ☐ Give information about the geographical location.
3 ☐ Use *and, but, because,* etc. to join her ideas together.
4 ☐ Say what kind of place Berlin is.

b Rewrite Jo's introduction. Look at the description of Madrid to help you.

Berlin is the capital city …

4 Rewrite Jo's conclusion. Replace the adjectives in bold with descriptive adjectives from exercise 2 or adjectives of your own choice.

Berlin is a **nice** [1] _wonderful_ city to visit. The people are **nice** [2] _____ . It's a **good** [3] _____ idea to visit Berlin during one of the many **nice** [4] _____ festivals, for example the Carnival. The Carnival is **nice** [5] _____ people wear **good** [6] _____ costumes and the music is **good** [7] _____ . You'll have a **good** [8] _____ time.

5 Read Jo's notes about Berlin. Choose four or five things to include in paragraphs 2 and 3. Decide which order you would write them.

Famous buildings and monuments/other things to see or do

- 50 theatres and 153 galleries ☐
- Museum Island – district with lots of museums ☐
- Charlottenburg Castle – a beautiful building ☑ 1
- Brandenburg Gate – a famous monument, lots of wide roads around it ☐
- two cathedrals ☐
- Hackescher Market – good for shopping + area around it has lots of clothes shops, cafes and galleries ☐
- Tiergarten – famous park ☐
- very good public transport ☐
- Tower in Alexanderplatz – 368m high views of city ☐

6 Complete the strategies box with the words below.

> description   grammar   include ✓   irrelevant

A description of a place

- Read the task carefully. Think about what information you can [1] _include_ in each paragraph. Make notes and decide which is the most interesting information. Eliminate [2] _____ or unnecessary information.
- Organise your notes into paragraphs.
- Use a variety of adjectives to make your [3] _____ more interesting. Avoid meaningless adjectives such as *good* or *nice*.
- Summarise what makes the place special and make recommendations.
- Check the number of words and then check your [4] _____ , punctuation and spelling.

7 Read the task and then write your description. Write about a city you have visited or about Berlin, using the information in exercises 3–5. Use the strategies in exercise 6 to help you. Write 200–250 words.

> - A tourist website is preparing descriptions of cities for visitors. Write a description of a city for the website.

Speaking

Directions

8 Match the questions 1–5 with the answers a–e.

1 Do you know where the bus station is?
2 Excuse me, I'm lost. Can you help me?
3 Excuse me, is the bus station near here?
4 How do I get to the bus station from here?
5 Excuse me, how do I get to Tate Modern?

a Go past the bus station and turn right. It's down that street, near the river.
b The bus station? No, I'm sorry I don't. I'm a visitor here too.
c Sure, where do you want to go?
d Yes, it is. It's just round the corner.
e Go straight on and then turn left after the bank.

9 Complete the dialogues with the phrases below. There are two extra phrases.

> do you know   How do I get
> just five minutes   turn right
> Thanks anyway   Excuse me ✓
> You're welcome   Go past

A: [1] _Excuse me_ , I'm looking for the National Museum.
B: I'm sorry, I don't know the museum.
A: [2] _____ .
A: Excuse me, [3] _____ the National Museum?
C: Ah, yes. It's in Dunbar Street, near the train station.
A: Is it near here?
C: Yes, it's [4] _____ from here.
A: How do I get there?
C: It's really easy. Go down this road and turn left. Then [5] _____ at the traffic lights and it's on your left.
A: Thanks very much.
C: [6] _____ .

6 meeting up

⊛ easy to do
⊛⊛ a bit harder
⊛⊛⊛ extra challenge

Vocabulary

Social relationships

1 Match 1–7 with a–g to make relationship phrases.

1	next-door	a	brother
2	distant	b	mate
3	great-	c	cousin
4	step-	d	pet
5	team	e	neighbour
6	family	f	boyfriend
7	ex-	g	aunt

2 Complete the text with the words from the box.

after   colleague   each   fell   friends   fun
get   kept   know ✓   laugh   out   up

This is a photo of my snowboarding friends. I got to ¹ _know_ them at a snowboard camp and we have ² _____ in touch through the internet. We meet from time to time. Alice goes ³ _____ with Tim; you can see they adore ⁴ _____ other. Last year they split ⁵ _____ , but only for a week. Kate and Alfie are close ⁶ _____ . They have a good ⁷ _____ together. Kate doesn't ⁸ _____ on with Ruby. I think they ⁹ _____ out because Ruby made ¹⁰ _____ of Alfie. Mike is a bit older than the others; he's Alfie's brother's ¹¹ _____ from work. He's really nice; he looked ¹² _____ me when I was ill at the camp.

Grammar

Present perfect with *for* and *since*

3 ⊛ Match questions 1–5 with answers a–e.

1 How long have you been friends with Julie?
2 How long did Laura go out with Adam?
3 How long have you had this watch?
4 How long did you play the piano?
5 How long have you lived in this house?

a Since my last birthday. It was a present.
b For five years, and then I stopped because I was too lazy to practise.
c Since we were in primary school together.
d For eight months. They split up after an argument.
e For ten years. It was built when I was six.

4 ⊛ Complete the sentences with *for* or *since*.

1 Harry and Jane have known each other _for_ two months.
2 Jan has lived in Prague _____ he was born.
3 We had our dog Blackie _____ a long time.
4 I've been here _____ last week.
5 My parents have been married _____ ages.
6 Luke travelled around the world _____ two years.

5 ⊛⊛ Put the words in the correct order to make sentences.

1 rabbit/years/had/three/a/~~Kate~~/pet/has/for
Kate _has had a pet rabbit for three years_ .
2 long/known/Steve/you/have/~~How~~
How _____ ?
3 since/~~I've~~/was/Budapest/lived/in/I/born
I've _____ .
4 Peggy/years/haven't/~~I~~/seen/five/for
I _____ .
5 has/last/~~Jack~~/since/Luke/with/friends/been/winter
Jack _____ .
6 recently/~~I~~/been/cinema/the/to/haven't
I _____ .
7 week/hundred/~~Mike~~/a/taken/photos/has/this
Mike _____ .

6 (✱✱✱) Complete the text with the correct form (present perfect or past simple) of the verbs in brackets.

My great-uncle Derek is a very interesting man. All his life he [1] _has been_ (be) interested in travelling and getting to know different countries. As a young man, he [2] _____ (study) at the University of Edinburgh for five years. Then he [3] _____ (find) a job in Barbados and he [4] _____ (work) there for six years. In the last thirty years, he [5] _____ (live) in nine countries and [6] _____ (learn) six languages. Since 2005 he [7] _____ (live) on a Greek island. He [8] _____ (have) a yacht for about ten years and recently he [9] _____ (sail) across the Atlantic.

Grammar plus: Time expressions for the recent past

7 (✱✱✱) Complete the sentences with the correct form (present perfect or past simple) of the verbs in brackets.

1 We _haven't been_ (not/be) anywhere exciting lately.

2 He _____ (leave) just a minute ago.

3 I _____ (not/do) very much work in the last few days.

4 I _____ (talk) to my distant cousin not long ago.

5 _____ (you/met) any interesting new people recently?

6 We _____ (see) several good films lately.

Grammar reference

Present perfect with *for* and *since*

We use the present perfect with *for* and *since* to talk about actions or situations which started in the past and continue into the present:

I've known Rachel *since 1998*. (I still know her.)
Robert *has lived* here *for five years*. (He still lives here.)

for and *since*

- We use *since* with a **point** in time (when the action started):

since 2005/Monday/last winter/her birthday/yesterday/ I was a child

- We use *for* with a **period** of time (the length of the time the action has taken):

for twenty minutes/three months/thirty years/ most of my life/a long time/ages

Questions with *How long …?*

- We can use *for* and *since* to answer the question *How long …?*:

'How long have you had this watch'? 'Since my birthday.' 'How long have you worked here?' 'For five years.'

- We can also use *for* and questions with *How long?* in the past simple to refer to actions or situations which happened in the past and are now finished:

'How long were they married?' 'They were married for twenty years.' (they're not married now → past simple)

'How long have they been married?' 'They've been married for twenty years.' (they're still married → present perfect)

Time expressions for the recent past

- We can use the present perfect with the following time expressions which refer to the recent past: *lately, recently, in the last few days*:

I haven't seen her recently.
Have you seen any interesting films lately?
I've read 200 pages of this novel in the last few days.

- We use the past simple with other time expressions which refer to the recent past: *not long ago, a minute ago*:

I visited Barcelona not long ago.
I saw them just a minute ago.

Vocabulary

Describing emotions

1 <u>Underline</u> the correct words to complete the sentences.

1 I feel <u>*depressed*</u>/*worried*. Nothing seems to be going well for me.

2 I opened the door of my flat and saw a thief inside. I've never been so *frightened/worried* in all my life!

3 We were all terribly *nervous/disappointed* when they cancelled the concert.

4 Adam's *annoyed/nervous* with his younger sister, because she's been playing with the things on his desk.

5 You mustn't feel *guilty/disappointed*. You haven't done anything wrong.

6 I'm *worried/jealous* about my brother. He looks very upset and I don't know why.

2 Complete the extract from Lily's diary with the words from the box.

> bored   embarrassed   excited ✓   guilty
> interested   jealous   nervous
> sympathetic   upset

MARCH

Saturday
Sophie's having a party on Saturday. I'm so ¹ <u>*excited*</u> . Will her cousin Oliver be there? He's so handsome! Actually, I'm ² _____ . Will he like me?

Sunday
It was horrible. Oliver danced with me, but he just looked ³ _____ . I'm sure he thinks I've got nothing interesting to say. I was so ⁴ _____ I almost cried.

Monday
I've talked to Lily. She was very ⁵ _____ and she said I mustn't worry: perhaps he was just ⁶ _____ and didn't know what to say.

Tuesday
Got an email from Oliver! He wants me to go out with him! He says 'we're both ⁷ _____ in the same things'.

Wednesday
Adam is ⁸ _____ because I'm going out with Oliver. But I split up with Adam a long time ago. Why is he trying to make me feel ⁹ _____ now?

Thursday

Grammar

Present perfect continuous

3 (✱) Complete the sentences with the present perfect continuous form of the verbs from the box.

> watch   study ✓   eat   write
> swim   repair

1 He<u>*'s been studying*</u> all night.

2 They _____ .

3 She _____ her bike.

4 They _____ a scary film.

5 She _____ Christmas cards.

6 He _____ chocolates.

4 (✱✱) <u>Underline</u> the correct form of the verbs to complete the sentences.

1 How many cakes have you <u>*bought*</u>/*been buying*?

2 Sorry to be late! Have you *waited/been waiting* long?

3 He's *worked/been working* on this painting for a month. It's almost ready.

4 I'm so sorry – I've *lost/been losing* your book.

5 My neighbour has *looked after/been looking after* her elderly mother for years.

6 Anne is sad today. She's *fallen out/ been falling out* with Patrick.

5 (✳✳) **Complete the sentences with the correct form (present perfect simple or present perfect continuous) of the verbs in brackets.**

1 I'm so tired. I _'ve been revising_ (revise) all day and I _haven't finished_ (not/finish) yet.

2 He _____ (travel) for many years. He _____ (visit) about fifty countries.

3 Sam _____ (cook) all afternoon. He _____ (prepare) a wonderful dinner.

4 This is one of the best films I _____ _____ (ever/see). I _____ (try) to get it on DVD for ages, but I can't find it.

5 I _____ (find) my mobile! I _____ (look for) it all morning!

6 Susan _____ (text) me a lot recently. She _____ (send) me about fifty texts this week!

6 (✳✳✳) **Complete the questions with the correct form (present perfect simple or present perfect continuous) of the verbs in brackets.**

1 Jessica is taking her driving test again tomorrow.

  a How long _has she been learning_ (learn) to drive?

  b How many times _has she taken_ (take) the test so far?

2 Fred is a filmmaker.

  a How long _____ (make) films?

  b How many films _____ (make)?

3 Greg works at a bank.

  a How long _____ (work) there?

  b How many other jobs _____ (have)?

4 Ellen and David have decided to get married.

  a How long _____ (go out) together?

  b _____ (buy) a flat yet?

Grammar reference

Present perfect continuous

Form

+	I/You/We/They	**have ('ve) been** waiting.
	He/She/It	**has ('s) been** waiting.
−	I/You/We/They	**have not (haven't) been** waiting.
	He/She/It	**has not (hasn't) been** waiting.
?	**Have** I/you/we/they	**been** waiting?
	Has he/she/it	

Short answers	Yes, I/you/we/they **have**.
	No, I/you/we/they **haven't**.
	Yes, he/she/it **has**.
	No, he/she/it **hasn't**.

Wh- questions

Why have you been waiting?
How long have you been waiting?

Use of present perfect continuous

• We use the present perfect continuous to talk about actions which started in the past and continue up to now:

*My brother **has been studying** chemistry since 2006.* (he's still studying chemistry)

• We also use the present perfect continuous to talk about activities from the recent past which have results/consequences in the present:

I feel tired. I've been painting my bedroom all day. (that's why I'm so tired)

Present perfect continuous and present perfect simple

• We use the present perfect simple to focus on the result of an activity (especially when answering the question *How much?* or *How many?*). We use the present perfect continuous to focus on the activity itself (especially when answering the question *How long?*):

I've read three books about ancient Egypt. (focus on the result of activity, *three books*)
I've been reading about ancient Egypt. (focus on the activity itself, *reading*)
They have played two matches. (How many? *two matches*)
They have been playing all morning. (How long? *all morning*)

• We use the present perfect continuous to talk about a repeated action over a period of time:

He's been texting me recently. (repeated action over a period of time)
He's texted me recently. (one completed action)

> **Notice!**
> We use the present perfect continuous with activity verbs. With state verbs (e.g. *know, have, understand, believe, like*) we can only use the present perfect simple.
>
> *We have been dancing for hours.* (*dance* is an activity verb)
> *I have always liked coffee.* (*like* is a state verb)

Reading

1 Read the title of the article and the headings and choose the best answer.

1 The text is
   a a newspaper article about being famous.
   b a newspaper article about how a couple met.
   c a newspaper article about relationships.

2 Find the words or phrases in the text and choose the correct meaning.

1 *announced*
   a made an advertisement
   b asked about
   c told the public

2 *deliriously happy*
   a extremely happy
   b a little bit happy
   c not happy at all

3 *propose*
   a to suggest a place to go out
   b to ask someone to marry you
   c to finish a relationship

4 *opening night*
   a the time of day when it becomes dark
   b the last time you can see a play/show
   c the first performance of a play/show

5 *accepted*
   a said 'yes' to a proposal
   b said 'no' to a proposal
   c said 'maybe' to a proposal

6 *couple*
   a one person
   b two people
   c three people

3 Read the text and tick (✓) true or cross (✗) false.

1 ☐ Jeremy works in finance.
2 ☐ Jeremy is more or less the same age as Connie.
3 ☐ Connie and Jeremy did not sit next to each other at the train station.
4 ☐ At first Connie was pleased that Jeremy was interested in her.
5 ☐ When Connie first looked at Jeremy she thought he was very attractive.

4 Read the text again and choose the correct answers.

1 It wasn't easy for Jeremy to find Connie because
   a she wouldn't give him her phone number or email address.
   b she didn't want him to know she was a famous singer.
   c he forgot what she looked like so he didn't recognise her.
   d he didn't know how to contact her in the beginning.

2 Connie
   a was already famous when she appeared on a TV talent show.
   b became famous in Britain after she was on the TV show.
   c is famous all over the world as a result of being on the TV show.
   d isn't very famous now, although she was on a TV talent show.

3 When Jeremy asked Connie to marry him
   a she was on stage singing in a show.
   b he didn't give her an engagement ring.
   c he was very romantic.
   d she didn't accept at first.

4 The couple
   a already know which date they are going to get married on.
   b have yet to decide the exact day for the wedding next year.
   c think they may get married in the next few years.
   d are definitely going to get married this year.

Connie in *The Sound of Music.*

LOVE TRAIN?

Sound of Music star Connie Fisher tells how she got to know her true love

Connie Fisher, 25, has just <u>announced</u> her engagement to Jeremy Reed, 40, an international banker from Barry, South Wales.

Love at first sight

Connie and Jeremy first met on a crowded station platform in Wales, last July. Connie was on the phone to her mum when she realised the man sitting next to her was interested in her. At first she was annoyed because she was feeling ill that day with a sore throat and headache. Connie explains: 'I had the feeling he was going to start talking to me and I thought:

Connie and Jeremy

"That's all I need, some guy trying to chat me up." We had a bit of a conversation but at first I didn't even look at him. Then … I turned round – and there was this gorgeous man!'

Connie said later: 'I am <u>deliriously happy</u> – I knew Jeremy was Mr Right from the moment I saw him.'

They chatted for a while, then left on different trains – without exchanging phone numbers or email addresses.

Detective work

Millions of people in Britain saw Connie win the TV talent show *How Do You Solve A Problem Like Maria?* She became famous all over the country after the show – but Jeremy had no idea who she was, or how to contact her. Then he remembered something she said during their conversation at the station. Connie mentioned that she was singing in a show in London's West End. So Jeremy asked a friend who works in show business to help him find her. Jeremy got in contact with Connie and they arranged to meet.

On their first date, Jeremy gave Connie a special present: a toy train, to remind her of their meeting at the station. The <u>couple</u> have been together since then.

A happy ending

After going out together for almost a year, Jeremy decided to <u>propose</u>. He asked Connie to marry him after the <u>opening night</u> of *The Sound of Music* in Cardiff. He got down on his knees and gave her a diamond ring in true romantic style! He was delighted when she <u>accepted</u>. The <u>couple</u> plan to marry some time next year.

* The West End is an area of London where there are lots of theatres with shows, similar to Broadway in New York.

Reading

Sentence completion

1 **In each pair, complete the second sentence with one or two words so that the meaning stays the same as the first.**

1 a What Jack enjoys about his work is being his own boss.

  b Jack likes his job because he's his own _____ .

2 a My interest in travelling began in my childhood.

  b I first became interested in travelling as a _____ .

3 a Van Gogh's art became popular after his death.

  b Before he _____ , Van Gogh's art was not popular.

4 a We were travelling from San Diego to Las Vegas that day.

  b Our destination on that day was _____ .

Exam TIP

Sometimes the word you need for the gap is used in the text, but the sentence is built differently. Sometimes you need a different part of speech, or a different word to express the same idea.

2 **Read the first paragraph of a story about Charlie and Eva. Complete sentences 1–3 with one or two words, according to the information in the story.**

Return from Iguazu Falls

Charlie and Eva adored each other, everyone knew that. They read the same books and watched the same films. They cooked, danced, and travelled together. One summer they cycled around the Mediterranean. Sometimes one of them travelled alone and then came back to tell the other the stories of their adventures. They always had something to talk about.

1 Charlie and Eva did a lot of things _____ .

2 They travelled around the Mediterranean by _____ .

3 Charlie and Eva could always find a topic to _____ about.

3 **Read the rest of the story and complete sentences 1–8 with one or two words, according to the information in the story.**

No-one understood why they fell out. Did they argue about politics? Or about the route of the bike trip across North Africa they were planning? One thing was clear: Charlie and Eva were no longer together.

No-one knew much about their feelings, either. Eva concentrated on her studies, and Charlie took his bike and flew to Argentina. He cycled around South America for five months. He saw mountains, deserts and tropical forests. He saw Iguazu Falls, a huge, roaring curtain of water surrounded by green jungle.

He came back one Saturday morning in September. As he cycled home, he realised he just *had* to tell Eva about his trip. Even though he was so tired from the journey, he simply couldn't stop himself. He turned into the street where she lived and nearly fell off his bike.

There was a large car in front of Eva's house, a car decorated with flowers, white ribbons and balloons. Charlie knew that car. It belonged to Jeremy, a guy he couldn't stand.

'No,' said Charlie to himself, 'please, no.'

At that moment the door opened and Eva rushed out, wearing a white dress, her long hair blowing in the wind, as beautiful as the Iguazu Falls. She saw Charlie and a smile lit up her face.

'Charlie! Thank God you're here! What a mess! No-one's remembered to pick up the wedding cake from the restaurant. Will you come with me and help me? I'd no idea what a nightmare organising a wedding is.'

Charlie stood there, unable to say a word.

'Why are you staring like that, Charlie? My sister Julia's marrying that idiot Jeremy. Can you believe it? Oh, it's so good to see you. It's been such a long time.'

And two arms in white silk closed around Charlie's dirty neck.

1 Some friends thought Eva and Charlie had an _____ about politics.

2 At the time they split up, Charlie and Eva were planning to travel to _____ .

3 Charlie spent _____ in South America.

4 Iguazu Falls are in a _____ .

5 Charlie returned in _____ .

6 Charlie was upset when he saw the _____ .

7 Eva had a problem because no-one had remembered to bring the _____ .

8 Eva was busy because her sister was getting _____ .

Listening

Multiple choice

4 (10) **Listen to the introduction to a programme about travelling to school and choose the best answer, a, b, c or d.**

The government wants to encourage children to travel to school on foot, by bike or by public transport rather than by car because

a ☐ it's good for their health.

b ☐ it helps the environment and the traffic.

c ☐ more than eight million children travel to school by car.

d ☐ the number of trips to school has increased.

5 (10) **Match the following explanations 1–4 to options a–d in exercise 4. Listen again if you need to.**

1 The answer is *wrong* because the speaker makes a similar statement about journeys *by car* only.

2 The answer is *wrong* because the number refers to *all* the children who travel to school.

3 The answer is *wrong* because this is only true about *two* of the solutions and not about all *three*.

4 The answer is *correct* because this is true about *all three* ways of getting to school.

Exam TIP

The wrong answers often appear similar to something in the recording, and may use the same words, but they are not the same. Listen out for the difference in meaning.

6 (11) **Read the questions. Listen to the rest of the programme. Choose the correct answers a, b, c or d.**

1 Walking is

  a always the best alternative to car transport.

  b the only healthy way of travelling to school.

  c made safer thanks to special lessons.

  d recommended when there is no bus.

2 On a walking bus children

  a follow a different route every day.

  b are looked after by older children.

  c have the opportunity to talk to each other.

  d don't carry their books.

3 To make cycling more attractive, schools can

  a create cycle lanes.

  b introduce low-speed zones.

  c close their car parks.

  d give students a safe place to leave their bikes.

Use of English

Gap fill

7 **Complete the sentences with the words from the box.**

> after   get ✓   jam   pass   pick   out
> transport

1 It's difficult to _get_ around this city without a car.

2 *Public* _____ in my town has improved a lot in the last five years.

3 Mum, can you _____ *me up* after school? I don't want to walk in this rain!

4 I've got a free *bus* _____ to go to and from school.

5 We *fell* _____ with our neighbours because our dogs can't stand each other.

6 There's a terrible *traffic* _____ .

7 When I was little, my grandma often *looked* _____ me.

8 **Which sentences in exercise 7 contain:**

• a multiword verb?   _1_ ___ ___

• a compound noun?   _2_ ___ ___

9 **Complete the text with one word in each gap.**

Exam TIP

The missing word in a gap-fill task may be one part of a multiword verb or of a compound noun. Looking at the words before and after the gap will help you.

I'm always surprised when parents pick [1] _up_ my sixteen-year-old classmates after school. I've [2] _____ travelling around the city since I was six! At first I travelled to school with my older sister and it was her job to [3] _____ after me. We had fun on the bus. If there was a [4] _____ jam, we counted all the cars that were red. We sometimes fell [5] _____ and then we would sit on the bus and not say a word. We switched [6] _____ our mp3 players and listened to music. We made this journey together [7] _____ three years, and then my sister went to a different school. By that time I knew where to [8] _____ on and off the bus. When I was twelve, I had no difficulty getting [9] _____ the city. [10] _____ I ever have children, I'll teach them to use [11] _____ transport when they're quite young.

Vocabulary & Grammar

1 Underline the correct words to complete the sentences.

1 *Global/Public* transport is not very reliable in my town.

2 You can reduce your carbon *footprint/pollution* by using the bus and train instead of the car.

3 My sister's taken my blouse without my permission again! I'm so *jealous/annoyed*!

4 Don't *waste/destroy* energy by boiling a full kettle of water for one cup of tea.

5 The plane to Paris was *cancelled/delayed*. We had to wait three hours.

6 You can save 10% on your heating bills by *turning down/switching off* your central heating by one degree.

7 I don't know her very well, she was just my *colleague/classmate* in secondary school.

8 Our father got married again and we have now two *step-/ex-* sisters.

/7

2 Complete the sentences with the correct form of the verbs in brackets. Circle *since* or *for* where necessary.

1 We _went_ (go) to the same school (for)/since a couple of months but then his family moved to London.

2 Pete's my best friend. We _____ (know) each other *since/for* primary school.

3 I _____ (think) about you a lot *since/for* we last met.

4 Tina _____ (learn) Spanish *since/for* six weeks but she can only say a few words.

5 His new book is fascinating. _____ (you/read) it?

6 Our teacher _____ (be) married *since/for* thirty years. Unfortunately, his wife died last year.

7 How long _____ (you/see) your new girlfriend?

/6

3 Complete the sentences with one word in each gap.

1 I had nothing to do and was really _bored_ .

2 We need more cycle _____ for cyclists to make our roads safer.

3 Manchester United's Ryan Giggs celebrated with his _____ mates after scoring the third goal.

4 The effect of _____ warming is more than just a rise in the world's temperature.

5 You can save both money and _____ by choosing more efficient cars or driving less.

6 There are lots of traffic _____ in Bangkok. People spend hours in their cars.

7 We've only just met. I'd like to _____ to know him better.

/6

4 Correct the mistakes in the sentences.

1 What will you do after school?
  What are you going to do after school?

2 I think our new teacher is going to be strict.
  _____

3 I'll get married when I'll be 25.
  _____

4 Ian's planned everything – he'll travel next year.
  _____

5 If it won't stop raining, we'll stay at home.
  _____

6 I won't talk to you if you apologise for being rude.
  _____

/5

5 Read the diary entry and choose the best answer.

/6

★ **31 DECEMBER**

I met Tom, my ex-boyfriend, through our [1](next door)/ distant neighbour's daughter, Lizzy. About two months ago, Lizzy [2]*gave / has given* him my phone number and he called. I was very [3]*nervous / upset* before our first date. But we had a good laugh together and [4]*fell out / got on* very well. After that first date I [5]*have seen / saw* Tom almost every day for three weeks. Then we had a big argument and decided to split [6]*up / off*. I'd like to keep in touch with him but I won't see him again [7]*unless / if* he gives me a call. He knows my telephone number!

Reading

6 Read the article about the UK government's campaign to save water and the statements below. Complete the gaps in each statement 1–7 with a maximum of three words, using the information in the text.

We all can and need to save water

The UK government has launched a campaign to encourage families to save water.

Half of households in England and Wales already suffer from 'water stress', where the demand for clean drinking water could soon be higher than the water available. The UK is known for its wet weather, but London actually has less annual rainfall than Paris or Rome. The water crisis is greatest in the South East where at least ten million people have less water per person than those living in much drier countries, such as Egypt and Morocco.

The average person in the UK uses a huge amount of water: about 150 litres a day compared to 127 litres per person in Germany. Now the Department for the Environment, Food and Rural Affairs (Defra) has launched a campaign to help every person save at least 20 litres of water a day. This could help to save millions of litres of water every year.

The campaign, launched by TV presenter Kate Humble, points out that saving water helps to cut bills. It will also help to tackle climate change by reducing energy use.

'Water is a precious resource but we all waste too much of it,' she said. 'Saving water at home doesn't need to be a big sacrifice – just spending one minute less in the shower can make a big difference. Simple changes like that can also help the environment. Using less water means saving on carbon emissions caused by transporting it to our taps.'

The campaign will include online advice and newspaper and radio advertising.

Some of Defra's top tips for saving water:
* Turn off the tap while you brush your teeth – saves six litres of water a minute.
* Cut your shower time by just one minute – saves nine litres of water.
* Use a bowl to wash the dishes rather than leave the tap running – saves up to six litres a minute.
* Use a watering can or a bucket to wash the car instead of a hosepipe – saves 16 litres a minute.

1 According to the government, people use too _much water_ .

2 Water shortage is the biggest problem in _____ .

3 The average person in Germany uses _____ water than the average person in the UK.

4 As a result of the campaign, both household bills and _____ will be lower.

5 Transporting less water to our homes will reduce _____ .

6 The government will promote the campaign through the media and _____ .

7 You'll save the most litres of water a minute if you follow Defra's advice when you _____ .

/6

Listening

7 (12) Listen to the conversation between Dave and Kate. Choose the correct answers.

1 Dave is Kate's ___ .
   a classmate   c brother
   b ex-boyfriend   d cousin

2 Kate has known Robert ___ .
   a since Christmas   c since Friday
   b for one week   d for two weeks

3 Dave was ___ when he heard of Kate's date with Robert.
   a annoyed   c worried
   b jealous   d disappointed

4 Dave will take Kate to his friend's party if she ___ .
   a starts to behave more sensibly
   b doesn't get on well with Robert
   c stops chatting with strangers online
   d doesn't go on a date with Robert

5 Kate seems ___ Dave's invitation.
   a excited about   c interested in
   b surprised by   d embarrassed by

6 Dave admits that he ___ .
   a has met lots of friends via the internet
   b has lied on the internet about his looks
   c likes his virtual friends very much
   d is not going to make friends online

/6

Communication

8 Complete the dialogues with one word in each gap.

1 A: E_xcuse_ me, how do I g_____ to the town centre from here?
   B: T_____ left at the traffic lights.

2 A: Thank you very m_____ for your help.
   B: You're w_____ .

3 A: Let me i_____ myself. My name's Ann Pitts.
   B: P_____ to meet you.

4 A: Sorry I c_____ help.
   B: Thanks a_____ .

/8

Marks

Vocabulary & Grammar	/30 marks
Reading	/6 marks
Listening	/6 marks
Communication	/8 marks
Total:	/50 marks

7 fast food

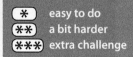

* easy to do
** a bit harder
*** extra challenge

Vocabulary

Preparing food

1 a Match the sentence beginnings 1–8 with the endings a–h.

1 Slice
2 Spread the marmalade
3 Pour in
4 Finally, add some pepper
5 Grill until
6 Blend all the ingredients
7 Peel the tomatoes and
8 Mix all the ingredients

a and serve.
b chop them.
c in a big bowl.
d on the bread.
e the onions.
f the milk.
g the grated cheese melts.
h with an electric blender.

b Match the sentences from exercise 1a to the pictures.

A `1e`

B ☐

C ☐

D ☐

E ☐

F ☐   G ☐   H ☐

Grammar

The passive

2 (*) <u>Underline</u> the correct form (active or passive) of the verbs to complete the sentences.

1 People in this village still _make/are made_ their own bread and cheese.
2 This box _hasn't opened/hasn't been opened_ for a hundred years.
3 The woman _took/was taken_ to hospital.
4 A new biography of Picasso _is writing/ is being written_.
5 This question cannot _answer/be answered_.
6 I hope your watch _will find/will be found_ soon.

3 (**) Complete the second sentence so that it means the same as the first.

1 People speak English all over the world.
   English _is spoken all over the world._
2 Someone has found the lost children.
   The lost children _____
3 A mechanic is repairing our car now.
   Our car _____
4 They taught him Russian at school.
   He _____
5 You can buy hot snacks here.
   Hot snacks can _____
6 We will build a new road next year.
   A new road _____

4 (**) Complete the text with the correct passive form of the verbs in brackets.

Chocolate robbery

Ten thousand bars of chocolate [1] _were stolen_ (steal) from the famous Penny Street chocolate factory last night. The robbery [2] _____ (discover) early this morning. Two young women [3] _____ (arrest) in connection with the crime and are being held at Tunbridge Street police station. Factory employees [4] _____ (question) by the police at the moment. The factory will remain closed today, but it will reopen tomorrow and our town's famous chocolate [5] _____ (produce) as usual.

5 (**) Complete the sentences with the correct passive form of the verbs from the box.

[drink   bring ✓   grow   grill   produce   serve   write]

1 Chocolate _was brought_ to Europe by the Spanish.
2 The first cookery books _____ in ancient times.
3 Parmigiano cheese _____ in Italy.
4 Tomatoes _____ in Europe since the 16th century.
5 The steaks _____ right now. Dinner _____ in ten minutes.
6 This smoothie should _____ very cold.

6 (***) Complete the text with the correct form (active or passive) of the verbs in brackets.

The Potato Website

Home   **The Potato**   **Recipes**   **Kids**   **About Us**   **News and Press**

The History of Potatoes

Potatoes ¹ _have been grown_ as a food for at least 7,000 years. They ² _____ (come) from South America, where they ³ _____ (grow) by the Incas 6,000 years ago. In the sixteenth century, the Spanish invaded what is now Peru and ⁴ _____ (bring) the potato plant back to Europe.

Today, potatoes ⁵ _____ (eat) all over the world. Over 300 million tonnes ⁶ _____ (produce) every year. They are cooked, baked, fried and made into soups and salads. (For recipes, click here.)

Nearly everywhere on earth people ⁷ _____ (eat) chips, or French fries. They ⁸ _____ (probably/invent) in Belgium, but now they are a symbol of global food. Frozen pre-cooked French fries ⁹ _____ (produce) since the 1970s. However, they are even less healthy than ordinary chips. Perhaps a healthy, low-fat variety of chips ¹⁰ _____ (invent) in the future.

Grammar reference

The passive

Form

To form the passive we use the verb *to be* in the correct tense + the past participle of the main verb.

Present simple	Milk **is delivered** to our house every day. How many languages **are spoken** in China?
Present continuous	A new shopping centre **is being built** in my city. More and more courses **are being taught** online.
Present perfect	A young singer **has been chosen** to represent England. Some beaches **have been closed** to swimmers because of high waves.
Past simple	Uranus **was discovered** by William Herschel in 1781. Some of the stolen goods **were found** in a nearby flat.
Future simple	Students **will be informed** of any changes by email. What time **will** dinner **be** served?
Passive with a modal verb	Dogs **shouldn't be left** on their own for long periods. All work **must be finished** before the end of April.

Use

- We use the passive when we are more interested in the action than in the person who does/did it:

*These shoes **are made** in France.* (it doesn't matter who makes them)

- We use the passive when we don't know or care who does the action (agent):

*Jim's mobile phone **was stolen**.* (we don't know who stole it)

- If we want to mention the agent, we use a phrase beginning with *by*:

*This picture **was painted by** Picasso.*
*Our website **is visited by** over 50,000 visitors a month.*

Passive structures are more common in formal and written English.

Vocabulary

Nutrition and health

1 **Complete the sentences with the names of the nutrients.**

1 Fresh fruit is one of the best sources of
  v _itamins_ .

2 Meat and fish are rich in p_____ .

3 Brown bread has more f_____ than
  white bread.

4 Tea contains nearly as much c_____
  as coffee.

5 Chips contain much more f_____ than
  boiled potatoes.

2 **Choose the *two* words which can complete each sentence.**

1 I've _a, c_ a lot of weight.

  a put on ✓ **b** got **c** lost ✓

2 I'm not feeling very well these days. I have _____
  most of the time.

  a headaches **b** no energy **c** sick

3 I feel _____ .

  a headache **b** sick **c** fit and healthy

4 Cheese contains a lot of _____ .

  a protein **b** fat **c** fibre

3 **Complete Jessica's New Year's resolutions with the words from the box.**

> caffeine fat fibre fit
> headache put on look ✓

My New Year's resolutions

I'm going to ¹ _look_ after myself better
this year!

1 I'm going to lose some weight.

2 I'm going to eat less ² _____ and
  more ³ _____ .

3 I'll try not to ⁴ _____ weight
  again next Christmas.

4 I'm going to exercise every day
  until I feel ⁵ _____ and healthy.

5 If I have a ⁶ _____ , I won't
  take painkillers. I'll go for a
  walk instead.

6 I'm going to have less ⁷ _____ :
  only one cup of coffee a day.

Signed: Jessica Williams

Grammar

have something done

4 ⊛ **Match problems 1–5 with solutions a–e.**

1 My jacket's dirty.

2 I've got problems with my eyes.

3 I don't like the colour of my hair.

4 My shoes are in a bad state.

5 The engine in the car is making a funny noise.

a I must have it checked.

b I'm going to have it dyed.

c I've got to have them repaired.

d I should have them tested.

e I must have it cleaned.

5 ⊛⊛ **Answer the questions using the correct form of *have something done*.**

1 Did you repair your bike yourself?

  No, _I had it repaired_ .

2 Did you wash your car yourself?

  No, _____ .

3 Are you going to pierce your ears yourself?

  No, _____ .

4 Do you usually paint your nails yourself?

  No, _____ .

6 ⊛⊛ **Complete the second sentence using the correct form of *have something done*.**

1 The cobbler has repaired my shoes for me.

  I _'ve had my shoes repaired_ .

2 The hairdresser has restyled Kathy's hair
  for her.

  Kathy _____ .

3 The beautician is going to wax Suzie's legs
  for her.

  Suzie _____ .

4 The dentist whitened Mr Crump's teeth for him
  last month.

  Mr Crump _____ .

5 I must ask the nurse to take my blood
  pressure for me.

  I must _____ .

6 I think I'll go to the doctor's and ask him to
  check my heart.

  I think I _____ .

7 (✱✱✱) Today is Wednesday. Complete the sentences about Sarah using *have something done*.

DECEMBER

Monday
new windscreen!! ✓

Tuesday
dentist (checkup) ✓

Wednesday
medical tests ✓

Thursday
tattoo ?!

Friday
haircut and wax

1 On Monday Sarah (windscreen in her car/replace) *had the windscreen in her car replaced* .

2 On Tuesday she (her teeth/check) _____ _____ .

3 She (just/ some medical tests/do) _____ _____ today.

4 Perhaps she (tattoo/do) _____ _____ on Thursday.

5 On Friday she (her hair/cut) _____ and (her legs/wax) _____ .

Grammar Plus: *needs + -ing*

8 (✱✱✱) Complete the sentences with *need(s) +-ing*, using the verbs from the box.

> clean   cut   mend   recharge
> throw out   wash ✓

1 There are a lot of dirty dishes in the sink.
  They *need washing* .

2 Your coat's dirty. It _____ .

3 'These socks have got holes in them.
  They _____.' 'They're in such a terrible state that I think they just
  _____!'

4 Our holiday video is too long. I _____ _____ .

5 My laptop's not working. I think the battery
  _____ .

Grammar reference

have something done

Form

To make sentences with *have something done* we use the verb *to have* in the correct tense + object + the past participle of the main verb.

Present simple	I **have my car serviced** every year.
Present	She **is having her eyes tested** by an optician.
Present perfect	We **have had this room painted** four times.
Past simple	He **had the engine fixed** yesterday.
will/won't	You **will have your coat cleaned** very quickly.
going to	Sheila **is going to have her hair cut** next week.
modal verb	You **should have your photograph taken** once again.

Use

We use *have* + object + past participle to say that we arranged for something to be done (by employing or asking somebody to do it):

I **had my bedroom redecorated** last year. (I employed somebody to do it)
I need to **have my car repaired**. (I need to employ a mechanic to do it for me)

Compare pairs of sentences:

I **had my watch fixed** yesterday. (somebody fixed it for me)
I **fixed my watch** yesterday. (I did it myself)

We **will put in** new windows next year. (we will do it ourselves)
We **will have new windows put in** next year. (we will hire somebody to do it for us)

need(s) + -ing

We use *need(s) + -ing* to say that it is necessary or important for something to be done. It is not important who does it:

*The garage door is very difficult to open, it **needs replacing**.* (= it needs to be replaced)
*Your trousers are dirty. They **need cleaning**.* (= they need to be cleaned)
*His hair is too long. It **needs cutting**.* (= it needs to be cut)

Vocabulary

Food around the world

1 Rearrange the letters in brackets to make words to complete the menu.

```
┌─────────────────────────────────────┐
│            MENU                      │
│                                      │
│            Starters                  │
│  Noodle soup with slices of ¹ tender │
│      (nedtre) chicken and vegetables │
│  ² _____ (vuryoas) pancakes      │
│           with seafood               │
│                                      │
│          Main courses                │
│    Fish of the day, ³ _____      │
│   (ridfe) or ⁴ _____ (ligerdl)   │
│     – with fresh vegetables          │
│    and ⁵ _____ (iscpyr) French   │
│              fries                   │
│   Steak with a ⁶ _____ (chri)    │
│    sauce with cream and mushrooms    │
│   and simple ⁷ _____ (dobeil)    │
│              potatoes                │
│  ⁸ _____ (spyci) chicken curry   │
│    with rice – it's hot hot hot!     │
│                                      │
│            Desserts                  │
│  Chocolate cake – it's ⁹ _____   │
│   (etwes) and perfect to finish      │
│            your meal!                │
│            Fresh fruit               │
└─────────────────────────────────────┘
```

2 Complete the text with one letter in each gap to make the correct food words.

In tonight's programme
I'm cooking some delicious seafood
¹ pan _ _ _ _ _ with a ² fi _ _ _ _ _ of fresh fish
and prawns. The pancakes are a local ³ spe _ _ _ _ _ _
in Thailand. You need some ⁴ sp _ _ _ _ to make the
dish hot, some ⁵ o _ _ to fry the pancakes and some
⁶ s _ _ _ and pepper to flavour, and the ingredients to
fill the pancake. If you want a cold pancake, you can fill
it with salad and make a ⁷ s _ _ _ _ with mayonnaise.
The pancakes make a great ⁸ sn _ _ _ if you're
feeling a little hungry, and they're
extremely ⁹ t _ _ _ _!

Reading

3 Read the first paragraph of the text on page 61 and choose the best title.

1 **Students around the world**

2 **School lunches**

3 **Are you healthy?**

4 Read the text and questions 1–6 below. Match the questions to the paragraphs A–F where you find the answer. Then answer the questions.

1 What does the vending machine in Simon's school sell?

Paragraph _B_ – _Yoghurt, soup and soft drinks._

2 Why are health experts in the UK concerned about packed lunches?

Paragraph ___ – _____

3 Which city does Sarah live in?

Paragraph ___ – _____

4 Does a typical packed lunch in the UK always contain some type of fruit?

Paragraph ___ – _____

5 Who is going to have grilled fish for lunch tomorrow?

Paragraph ___ – _____

6 How many canteens sell hot food in the Thai school?

Paragraph ___ – _____

5 Read the text again. Tick (✓) true or cross (✗) false.

1 ☐ Most British students bring a packed lunch to school.

2 ☐ There are no vending machines in the school in Belgium.

3 ☐ If you want noodles at Ling's school you have to eat in one of the canteens.

4 ☐ In Finland, students do not have to pay for school lunches.

5 ☐ At Sarah's school, the salads often sell out early.

6 ☐ According to the nutrition expert, a sandwich at lunchtime is plenty to eat.

6 Where do you have lunch? What do you eat? Write a short paragraph about a typical lunch for you.

_____

_____

_____

_____

A vending machine

A canteen

In the UK, almost all secondary students stay at school for lunch. However, only about half the students eat a hot meal in the school canteen. The others bring a packed lunch to school. Typical packed lunches contain a sandwich, a fizzy drink, a chocolate bar or crisps – and maybe some fruit. However, many health experts are concerned that most packed lunches aren't nutritious enough – they lack protein, fibre and vitamins and the fat and sugar content is too high. Is it true? Four students tell us about their school lunches and our nutrition expert comments.

What students say ...

My friends and I all bring sandwiches for lunch. Most students also bring in some type of sweet or biscuit – they're good for energy. The only vending machine we have in school sells yoghurt, soup or a soft drink. There's a canteen, but it's not popular.
Simon, Antwerp, Belgium

Nearly all the students and staff eat in school. We have: a noodle bar which is open all day; a snack bar that serves fruit, sandwiches, pizza and ice cream, and two lunchtime canteens that sell hot lunches (the food is often spicy!) with fresh salad and vegetarian meals.
Ling, Bangkok, Thailand

School lunches are free. The food is usually healthy, and menus are planned to provide a balanced meal. In most towns, the week's menu for each school is printed in the local newspaper so parents can check what their kids are eating – tomorrow I'll be eating grilled fish with vegetables!
Thomas, Helsinki, Finland

I go to secondary school in London. The vending machines don't sell fizzy drinks now, only fruit drinks, low-fat milkshakes or water. In the canteen you can buy pasta, salads (they're always fresh and crispy) and sandwiches, but they sell out – if you're late, there are only greasy chips and burgers left!
Sarah, UK

What the expert says ...

A sandwich at lunchtime is not enough for a teenager. You may find it hard to concentrate and not have enough energy. You shouldn't depend on sweets and chocolate for energy – your energy level will drop suddenly later. Unhealthy packed lunches can also encourage bad eating habits. It's better to sit down and eat a proper meal. Pasta or noodles and salads provide enough carbohydrates for energy and vitamins. Chips and burgers or pizza every day is really unhealthy! You're likely to put on weight and your skin will suffer.

Listening

7 (13) **Listen to a presenter's introduction to a TV programme. Choose the best answer.**

1 On the programme the presenter is going to talk to
  a teenagers from different countries about their lunches.
  b a nutritionist about the health benefits of different food.
  c people from different countries about traditional food.

8 (14) **Listen to the rest of the programme and match speakers 1–5 with five of the statements a–e. There is one extra statement.**

1 ☐ Nico says that   3 ☐ Peter says that
2 ☐ Laura says that   4 ☐ Victoria says that

a some kids pay for fast food meals, although there are free meals.
b he/she likes the meals that are served at lunchtime.
c it is a good idea for schools to promote healthy eating attitudes.
d the food was not as good as home-made food, but it was very healthy.
e vending machines that sell fizzy drinks shouldn't be allowed in schools.

9 (14) **Listen again and choose the correct answers.**

1 At Nico's primary school
  a not many children brought packed lunches to school.
  b most children were allowed to bring sweets to school.
  c everyone had to eat fruit and brown bread.
  d the only drink the school sold was milk.

2 In Laura's country
  a schools don't give students a free breakfast.
  b the free lunches do not include fast food.
  c young people never eat fast food.
  d there are free fast food options for students who want them.

3 In Peter's opinion school meals nowadays
  a are better than a few years ago.
  b are worse than they were a few years ago.
  c include too many vegetables and salads.
  d should include things like pizza and burgers.

4 Victoria says that school meals always included
  a some kind of soup.
  b some kind of carbohydrate.
  c sweets and pastries.
  d a meat dish.

fast food

Writing

A formal letter of enquiry

1 Write your address and the date in the top right corner.

2 Write the address of the person or organisation you are writing to on the left.

3 Begin the letter *Dear Sir or Madam* if you don't know the name of the person you are writing to. If you know the name, begin *Dear + name*.

4 In **paragraph 1**, say why you are writing and if necessary explain who you are:
I am writing in relation to ...
I read about your facilities on your website and ...
a *I am writing with regard to your advertisement ...*
b _____

5 In **paragraph 2**, say what you require:
We would like to use the hall to hold a talent show ...
c _____
d _____
Ask for the information you need:
Please could you se. details of ...
When is the theatre hall/speaker/accommodation available?

6 Say that you expec a reply:
I look forward to hearing from you soon / in the near future ...
I would like to invite you to give a talk ...
e _____
f _____

7 Close the letter wit *Yours faithfully* if yc began it with *Dear Sir or Madam*. If you used *Dear + name,* close the letter wit *Yours sincerely.*

8 Sign the letter and then print your name or write it in CAPITAL LETTERS.

Sharples High School
15–19 Bourne Road
Manchester
M2 3RN
23 September 2010

The Manager
Harwood Theatre
27 Bromley Road
Manchester
M2 5RF

Dear Ms Hart,

We are a group of students from year 10 at Sharples High School and we are writing to enquire about the possibility of using the theatre facilities.

We are a school theatre group and we are preparing a production of Uncle Vanya. Unfortunately, the school theatre was damaged by fire last week and we urgently need another theatre. The performances would be 1–4 October from 2.30–4.30 p.m. Please could you tell us if the theatre is available at this time? We would also like to know how much it costs. Finally, could you please tell us if the theatre staff are available on these dates or if we could bring our own volunteer staff?

We look forward to hearing from you,

Yours sincerely,

Chris Stevens

Chris Stevens

1 Read the letter and choose the correct answers.

1 The students are writing because they want to
  a visit the theatre.
  b use the theatre.

2 They can't use the school theatre because
  a it is too small.
  b there was a fire there.

3 The students ask about
  a the availability, the cost and the staff.
  b the availability and the cost only.

2 Complete the examples a–f in the letter notes 1–8 above with the expressions below. Read the letter again to help you.

I am writing with regard to your advertisement ... ✓
We need a rehearsal venue ...
I look forward to your reply ...
Could you tell me if ...
I'd like further information about ...
I am a musician and I am writing in connection with ...

3 Match sentence beginnings 1–6 with endings a–f. Then say in which paragraph of a formal letter of enquiry you would find the sentences.

1 I saw your advertisement
2 I look forward
3 Could you tell me
4 Finally, please tell me
5 I am writing to enquire
6 I would also like to know if

a the price of a room for a week?
b about the accommodation.
c to your prompt reply.
d there are any restaurants near the house.
e for rooms to rent in the centre of Edinburgh.
f if the house is near public transport.

Paragraph 1: ___   Paragraph 2: ___   Paragraph 3: _2_

4 Complete the strategies box with the words below.

> sign off   in the correct places ✓   the information
> an answer

A formal letter of enquiry

- Write the addresses and the date ¹ _in the correct places_ .
- Give your reason for writing in paragraph 1.
- Ask for all ² _____ you need in paragraph 2. Remember to use polite question forms (*Could you … Please could you … I would like to know …* etc).
- Show that you expect ³ _____ in paragraph 3.
- Don't forget to ⁴ _____ correctly.
- Check the number of words and then check your grammar, vocabulary and spelling.

5 Read the task and then write your letter. Use the ideas in exercises 2 and 3 and the strategies in exercise 4 to help you. Write 120–150 words.

> You are planning to visit London for a week. You have seen an advertisement for rooms to rent for a short time. Write a letter of enquiry to Ms Jameson, 14 Tyne Road, London, NW1 3JN.
>
> - Explain your reason for writing.
> - Give the dates when you would like to stay, ask if there are rooms available and the cost.
> - Ask for information about the location of the hotel and how long it takes to travel into the centre.
> - Ask if there is a restaurant nearby and if the hotel has childcare facilities.

Speaking

Requests and offers

6 Match the situations 1–5 with the appropriate response a–e.

1 Your mother has just helped you to do something.
2 Your teacher has asked you to carry some books for him/her.
3 Your sister has offered to help you cook.
4 Your teacher has just offered to explain something again.
5 Your friend doesn't understand his/her homework.

a Thanks. Could you wash the vegetables?
b Shall I help you with that?
c Yes, no problem. Shall I put them over here?
d Thanks a lot.
e Thanks, that's very kind of you.

7 Ann is helping Bob to get ready for a party. Complete the dialogue with the phrases below.

> Can you put   Could you
> Is there anything
> Do you want me to do ✓
> Would you mind
> very kind of you   Shall I

Ann: ¹ _Do you want me to do_ something?

Bob: Yes, please. ² _____ the drinks on the table in the living room?

Ann: Sure, no problem. Okay, that's done. ³ _____ else?

Bob: Yes. ⁴ _____ move those chairs?

Ann: Yes, all right. Okay … I've moved the chairs. ⁵ _____ move the sofa too?

Bob: No, it's all right. I'll do that with my brother later. ⁶ _____ helping me with the food?

Ann: Okay.

Bob: That's ⁷ _____ .

8 living space

✱	easy to do
✱✱	a bit harder
✱✱✱	extra challenge

Vocabulary

Describing buildings

1 Find and correct six mistakes in the description of a house.

It's a ~~three-storey~~ terraced house. It looks very modern. It's got a balcony on the second floor. The windows on the ground floor are very small. There are two chimneys on the roof.

1 _two-storey_ 3 _____ 5 _____

2 _____ 4 _____ 6 _____

2 Complete the conversation between Lily and Ella with the words from the box.

> apartment block   attic   balcony   basement
> first floor   fun   ground   overlooks   roof
> detached ✓   storeys   traditional

Ella: Hi, Lily, it's Ella. Guess what? I'm calling from our new house.

Lily: Oh hi, Ella. That's fantastic! So what's your new house like? I want to hear all about it!

Ella: Well, it's a ¹ _detached_ house with two ² _____ .
Quite a ³ _____ house, in fact.

Lily: What's it like inside?

Ella: When you come in, there's a very big living room on the ⁴ _____ floor. It's perfect for parties. My bedroom's upstairs on the ⁵ _____ . It's lovely.
It ⁶ _____ the garden and it's got a little ⁷ _____ where I can stand and look at the sunset.

Lily: Sounds wonderful! Tell me more.

Ella: At the top of the house there's quite a big ⁸ _____ room where we're going to have a home cinema. And there's a ⁹ _____ where Dad and Jamie are going to put their pool table.

Lily: So is it ¹⁰ _____ to live in?

Ella: Sure. It's a lot better than living in an ¹¹ _____ .

Grammar

First and second conditional

3 ✱ Match the sentence beginnings 1–6 with the endings a–f.

1 If you didn't smoke so much,
2 If I had enough time,
3 If Jim was nicer to people,
4 If she spoke good English,
5 If we had a bigger house,
6 If I were you,

a he'd have more friends.
b I wouldn't trust that man.
c I'd do some sport regularly.
d she'd have a better job.
e we'd invite a lot of guests.
f you wouldn't have a cough all the time.

4 ✱ Choose the correct form of the verb, a, b or c to complete the sentences.

1 She'll be sick if she _b_ all those chocolates.
   a eat   b eats ✓   c will eat

2 I ___ a new car if I got a pay rise.
   a buy   b 'll buy   c 'd buy

3 If the bus ___ , we'll be late.
   a doesn't come   b won't come
   c didn't come

4 What would you do if you ___ someone stealing in a shop?
   a would see   b see   c saw

5 If he takes my advice, everything ___ well.
   a would go   b goes
   c will go

6 Brighton would be ideal for a holiday if there ___ so many people there.
   a aren't   b weren't   c wasn't

5 (✳✳) Complete the sentences with the correct form of the verb in brackets.

1 If I _knew_ (know) how to get there, I wouldn't ask.

2 You'll break it if you _____ (not/be) careful.

3 If she _____ (tell) him my secret, I'll never speak to her again.

4 If Chris was here, he _____ (know) what to do.

5 They'd be silly if they _____ (not take) this opportunity.

6 What _____ (you/do) if you locked yourself out of your flat?

6 (✳✳) Put the words in the correct order to make sentences.

1 gets/have/If/the/weather/picnic/better/we'll/a

If _the weather gets better, we'll have a picnic_ .

2 I/say/you/were/anything/wouldn't/if/I

I _____ .

3 don't/scream/that/I'll/radio/they/If/turn down

If _____ .

4 by a dog/were/if/do/attacked/What/would/you/you

What _____ ?

5 them/will/nobody/they/do/What/helps/if

What _____ ?

7 (✳✳✳) Complete the second sentence so that it has a similar meaning to the first.

1 You feel so lonely because you don't go out much.

If you _went out more, you wouldn't feel_ so lonely.

2 We haven't got any cheese, so we can't make a pizza.

If we _____ a pizza.

3 Matthew's overweight because he eats too much fast food.

If Matthew _____ overweight.

4 My father works very hard, so he can't go to the match with us.

If my father _____ to the match with us.

5 We aren't rich, so we can't buy a big house with a garden.

If we _____ a big house with a garden.

Grammar reference

First and second conditional

Form of first conditional

Condition if + present simple	Result will/won't + verb
If the weather **is** good,	we'll (= will) **go** for a walk.
If you **don't call** me tonight,	I'll (= will) **call** you on Monday.
If they **don't finish** their work,	they **won't** (= will not) **get** the money.
If I **help** you with your homework,	**will** you **wash** the dishes?

- We can begin the sentence with a condition (if- clause) or with a result (the main clause). After if we use the present tense, not the future:

If you **come** tomorrow, my mum **will bake** a cake.
My mum **will bake** a cake if you **come** tomorrow.

Use of first conditional

- We use the first conditional to talk about real possibilities in the future:

I'll **come** if they **invite** me.
If you **ask** Monica, she'll **tell** you everything.

Form of second conditional

Condition if + past simple	Result would/wouldn't + verb (infinitive without to)
If I **had** more time,	I'd (= would) **read** more.
If he **was** more organised,	he **wouldn't be** (= would not) late for school every day.
If you **didn't spend** so much money,	you'd (= would) **have** more savings.
If you **won** the lottery,	**would** you **buy** a sports car?

- We can begin the sentence with a condition (if- clause) or with a result (the main clause). After if we use the past simple:

If I **had** more money, I'd **buy** a new car.
I'd **buy** a new car if I **had** more money.)

Notice!
We put a comma (,) only when we start the sentence with the if- clause.
If it rains, we'll go to the cinema.

Use of second conditional

- We use the second conditional to talk about imaginary situations in the present or unlikely situations in the future:

If they **were** taller, they **would play** basketball on our school team. (but they are not taller)
If Tom **knew** her email address, he **would write** to her. (but he doesn't know her email address)

Vocabulary

Living together

1 Match words 1–6 with a–f to make collocations.

1 borrow
2 make
3 be
4 knock
5 share
6 let

a a mess/noises
b things without asking
c the chores
d somebody use the computer
e fussy/tidy
f on the door

2 Alex and Andy are flatmates, but they don't get on very well. Complete their complaints with the words from the box.

[borrows chores fussy ✓ knocking let mess nagging noises]

Alex is so annoying!
He's too ¹ _fussy_ and tidy. He keeps
² _____ me to tidy up. He comes into
my room without ³ _____ on the door and
tells me to open the window. We've only got
one computer, and he won't ⁴ _____
me use it, because he's on it
most of the time.

Andy's so annoying! He makes
a ⁵ _____ around the house and
doesn't clean up after himself. He doesn't
share the ⁶ _____ at all. He ⁷ _____
my things without asking. And he makes
annoying ⁸ _____ when he's
playing computer games!

Grammar

wish + past simple/*would*

3 ✱ Complete the wishes with the correct form of verbs from the box.

[like know have can
be ✓ be]

1 I wish Bill _was_ here. I need him to help me.
2 Johnny has to go to school. He wishes he _____ stay at home.
3 My computer's crashed. I wish I _____ how to repair it.
4 Zoe likes animals. She wishes she _____ a pet.
5 Our neighbours hate us! I wish they _____ us.
6 I don't like this weather. I wish it _____ warmer.

4 ✱✱ Read the situations and complete each wish, using the past simple.

1 I haven't got a brother.
I wish I _had_ a brother.
2 Alice lives in a big city and she doesn't like it.
Alice wishes she _____ in the countryside.
3 I have to work at the weekend.
I wish I _____ to work at the weekend.
4 Polly is the smallest girl in her class and she's not happy about it.
Polly wishes she _____ taller.
5 I can't play any musical instrument.
I wish I _____ play a musical instrument.
6 It rains a lot here.
I wish it _____ so much.

5 (✱✱) Mrs Williams and Mrs Dobson are sisters. They are talking about their teenage children, Michelle, Charlie and Kitty. Complete their wishes using *would*.

Mrs W: Michelle's been shopping again. She's bought herself another jacket. I wish she ¹ *wouldn't spend* (not/spend) so much money on clothes.

Mrs D: I know what you mean. Teenagers are so expensive! Phone bills, for example … I wish Kitty ² _____ (spend) less time talking on the phone.

Mrs W: Oh yes. Charlie's not like that, though. He doesn't need a lot of things. But I wish he ³ _____ (not/play) loud music at midnight. And I wish he ⁴ _____ (study) a bit more.

Mrs D: Kitty's doing okay at school, fortunately. But I wish she ⁵ _____ (help) with housework sometimes!

Mrs W: You can say that again … I wish Michelle and Charlie ⁶ _____ (clean) their own rooms at least.

Mrs D: But they're really sweet kids actually, aren't they?

Mrs W: Oh yes, they're great. I'm sure they'll learn these things in time. Do you remember what we were like at their age? Mum used to say 'I wish you ⁷ _____ (not/keep) *all* your clothes on the floor'!

Grammar plus: Expressing regret

6 (✱✱✱) Complete the sentences with the correct form of the verb in brackets.

1 If only mum _was_ (be) here!
2 Does Jack regret _____ (not tell) his father the truth?
3 If only my parents _____ (like) my boyfriend!
4 I don't regret _____ (choose) this school.
5 If only I _____ (not/feel) so nervous!
6 Mr Jones regrets _____ (buy) this car.

Grammar reference

wish + past simple/*would*

wish + past simple

- We use *wish* + past simple to talk about present situations that we are unhappy about. We don't think these situations will change:

*I **wish** we **could** stay here longer.* (but we can't)

wish + would

- We use *wish* + *would* + verb to talk about present situations that we are unhappy about. We think these situations could change. We often use it to talk or complain about something annoying:

*I **wish** he **would stop** shouting at me.* (he shouts at me and it annoys me)
*I **wish** you **wouldn't drive** so fast.* (you drive fast and I don't like it)
*I **wish** my boyfriend **would buy** me flowers from time to time.* (he doesn't buy me flowers and I'd like him to)

Expressing regret

- We use *if only* + past simple to express regret:

***If only** I **had** a younger sister.* (but I don't have a younger sister)

- We use *regret* + (*not*) *-ing* to talk about past situations that we are unhappy about:

*I **regret inviting** them to my birthday party.* (I'm sorry I invited them to my birthday party)
*I **regret not calling** Barbara yesterday.* (I'm sorry I didn't call Barbara yesterday)

Vocabulary

1 Complete the table with the adjective forms where possible.

Noun	Adjective with -ful	Adjective with -less
beauty	¹ _beautiful_	–
mind	² _____	³ _____
success	⁴ _____	–
⁵ _____	harmful	⁶ _____
wonder	⁷ _____	–
stress	⁸ _____	–
point	–	⁹ _____
¹⁰ _____	¹¹ _____	thoughtless
¹² _____	¹³ _____	careless
need	–	¹⁴ _____

2 Complete the sentences with adjectives from exercise 1.

1 Angelina Jolie is very attractive, in fact I think she's _beautiful_ .

2 Smoking is bad for you, it's _____ to the body.

3 Pete's work has lots of mistakes and it's untidy. He's very _____ .

4 It wasn't necessary for Kate to come – it was _____ because she couldn't help.

5 This TV programme is completely _____ , you don't have to think at all!

6 Jane works very hard and she works long hours. Her job is very _____ .

7 This food is _____ ! It's so tasty and well-cooked.

8 That animal isn't at all dangerous, it's totally _____ .

Reading

3 Read the text on page 69 quickly and choose the best answer.

1 The text describes different ways for teenagers to improve their bedrooms.

2 The text tells teenagers how important it is to decorate different areas of their rooms.

4 Read the text again and the problems below. Match the problems 1–7 to the correct solutions in paragraphs A–F. There is one extra problem that doesn't have a solution.

1 'I wish my parents would let me paint my room! I hate the colour.'
Rachel, 15

2 'I wouldn't know where to start! I can't even see my bedroom floor ... it's covered with my clothes and books ... '
Karen, 16

3 'I have to share a bedroom with my brother. It's a big room, but I feel like I don't have my own space. I wish I had my own bedroom!'
Josh, 16

4 'I don't know what to do! If I had more ideas, I'd change my room, but I don't want it to look silly. Help!'
Jackie, 14

5 'My parents won't let me have a TV in my bedroom. All my friends have TVs – I wish my parents would agree.'
Mike, 15

6 'I hate studying in my room ... my desk is always covered with stuff.'
Peter, 15

7 'My walls are really boring. There's nothing on them.'
Mark, 14

5 Read the text again and tick (✓) true or cross (✗) false.

1 ☐ The writer thinks the ideas most teens have about decorating horrify their parents.

2 ☐ You should buy cushions to decorate your bed because it's cheap.

3 ☐ It's a good idea to try out colours and patterns first before deciding.

4 ☐ Keeping your desk free of clutter is good because you'll find it easier to work.

5 ☐ You should keep big plastic boxes under your bed and not in the wardrobe.

6 ☐ It isn't a good idea to use curtains to divide rooms into separate areas.

a room of my own

When you're a teenager, your bedroom is where you sleep, study and hang out with your friends. It's a private space where you can listen to music, hang crazy posters on the walls and enjoy spending time. Creating your own space is not easy, especially if you share a room. But, decorating doesn't have to be difficult or expensive – or horrify your parents! Read our hot tips …

A Agree a budget and plan

Talk to your parents, tell them you would like to decorate your bedroom. Decide together how much you'll be able to spend and what you'll be able to change. For example, if they're not happy about you painting the whole room, ask to paint one wall. It's cheaper and you can make a feature of it.

B Make it your own

Want to make your bed stand out? Buy cushions or a cool bedspread – it won't cost much and it'll look good. Or try big floor cushions – they look cool and they're great for relaxing with friends. Put up posters of your favourite sports or pop stars.

C Experiment with different ideas

You've got to live in it! Choose styles, colours, patterns and accessories that you like (not your parents or friends). Look in magazines and on the internet for ideas. Experiment before you make any decisions. If colours and accessories aren't your thing, then you could make a feature of your sports trophies or your CD collection.

D Divide it up

If your room is big enough, you can create different areas by dividing it up – a study area, a place to sit and listen to music, your sleeping area … Use curtains or screens* to divide the space. This is a great solution too if you have to share a room – at least you'll each have your own space.

E Organise your study area

Make it a good space to work in. Put up plenty of shelves to store books so you can keep the desk clear – it's easier to work if there isn't any mess! Drawers under the desk are a good idea to keep all the bits and pieces you need, too. If you can't buy new furniture, then use cardboard boxes painted in different colours.

F Keep it tidy!

Is your room always a mess? Find storage options that are easy for you to use. For example, big plastic boxes with tops that you can keep under your bed or more shelves in your wardrobe.

*screen – a flat piece of wood or material used to separate one area of a room from another

exam trainer 4

Reading

Matching questions

1 Read the title and introduction to a magazine interview to find out what it is about. Who do you think the text is for?

  a experienced cooks

  b people who can't cook

food · food · food · food · food · food · food

Teaching yourself how to cook

The best way to make sure you always get good food is to learn to cook it yourself. Johnny Buttimer, TV chef and food writer, tells you how to start.

2 **a** Read the first paragraph of the interview. What is it about?

  a ☐ typical food on sailing trips

  b ☐ Johnny's parents and cooking

  c ☐ why Johnny learned to cook

"I've always enjoyed good food. Both my parents cook very well. When I was fifteen I went on a sailing holiday with some friends. After three days of eating instant soups and stuff out of tins I said to myself, 'I've had enough'. I knew nobody was going to cook nice meals for me on the boat, so the only solution was to learn to do it myself. So that's what I did.

b Choose the question a–c, which Johnny answers in the first paragraph of the interview above.

  a ☐ What's a typical menu on a sailing trip?

  b ☐ How did your cooking adventure begin?

  c ☐ Were your family good cooks as well?

3 Read the rest of the interview. Match questions a–e to paragraphs 1–4. There is one extra question.

  a How can you start learning if you know nothing about cooking?

  b What are the advantages of knowing how to cook when you're eighteen?

  c What menu would you recommend for a teenage house party?

  d Where can you find good recipes?

  e Which dishes are the best to begin with?

1 _____

You can eat well wherever you are, and you don't depend on anyone. You can invite your friends and offer them something better than crisps and fizzy drinks. And some day you'll start living on your own and then you'll really feel the difference. It's no fun eating sandwiches and burgers every day. Also, cooking with fresh ingredients is cheaper than buying ready-made food.

2 _____

Well, one way is to watch someone cooking simple dishes. Help them, and ask questions. You can also buy yourself a simple cookbook for beginners, the kind that explains everything from the start, including how to boil an egg.

3 _____

Salads are great for a start, because they don't need cooking. If you're eating a salad you like, you can actually learn to copy it by seeing what's in it and then using the same ingredients. Pasta is another good option. It's easy to cook and can be served with hundreds of delicious, easy-to-make sauces which make it a different dish every time. Baked potatoes are good too: you can prepare them in lots of ways, with different fillings.

4 _____

Probably not in large cookbooks at first; you may find them too difficult. But there are simpler cookbooks around, with titles such as Cooking for Beginners or Simple Pasta Recipes. There are also good recipes in magazines – especially men's magazines – they're simple and take little time to prepare. And you can learn a lot from chatting with other people who cook."

70

Listening

Multiple choice

4 (0) **Listen to Alex telling his sister, Laura about his flatmate, Andy. Try to answer these questions.**

a Why is Alex annoyed? _____

b In Laura's opinion, what is the main problem? _____

5 (0) **Listen again and choose the correct answer.**

1 Alex is annoyed because Andy
   a doesn't do his share of the chores.
   b makes a fuss over nothing.

2 Laura thinks the problem is
   a Andy has never done any cleaning.
   b They have different needs.

Exam TIP

In multiple choice tasks sometimes you have to answer questions about a speaker's opinion, feelings or intentions. Work these out from a whole passage rather than from one sentence.

6 (0) **Listen to a conversation between Laura, Alex and Andy. Choose the correct answers.**

1 Laura is trying to
   a change the agreed cleaning time.
   b make Andy clean the bathroom.
   c help the boys to agree.

2 The thing Andy dislikes most is
   a cleaning the living room.
   b being reminded to do the cleaning.
   c doing housework when he's ill.

3 Alex
   a thinks Andy shouldn't eat in the living room.
   b criticises Andy's mum.
   c wants Andy to clean the living room at least a bit.

4 At the end
   a Alex and Andy reach agreement.
   b they cannot agree about the bathroom.
   c they are confused by Laura's suggestions.

Use of English

Gap fill

7 **a Choose the correct answer a, b or c to complete this sentence.**

My parents want me to look ___ my little brother on Saturday.

a at   b after   c for

b Look at the two *wrong* answers in exercise 7a. Match them to these sentences.

1 I'm looking ___ a holiday job.

2 You've been looking ___ this painting for fifteen minutes!

8 **Read the two groups of sentences. In each group, match the answers a–c to the sentences 1–3.**

A 1 Jim ___ science fiction stories for eight years.
   2 He ___ the first one when he was ten.
   3 Since then, he ___ more than twenty.

a wrote   b has written   c has been writing

B 1 I'm waiting here because my car ___ .
   2 The washing machine ___ and can be used.
   3 Every time this computer ___ I wonder if it wouldn't be cheaper t o buy a new one!

a has been repaired   b is repaired   c is being repaired

Exam TIP

To choose the correct answer in a gap-fill task, look at the structure of the whole sentence. To eliminate the wrong answers, think of the structures in which they would be correct.

9 **Choose the correct answer a, b or c to complete the text.**

I didn't realise I was a computer addict until last Thursday, when my computer broke down and the computer repair man ¹ _a_ it away. It's Tuesday now, so I ² ___ without a computer for four days. I've been looking ³ ___ things to do while it ⁴ ___ . I've been talking to friends ⁵ ___ the phone. I ⁶ ___ eleven films. I've ⁷ ___ and paid a shocking sum for it. I've spent many hours sitting and thinking about the games I ⁸ ___ if I had my computer back. I've fallen ⁹ ___ with my brother over nothing, simply because I'm so stressed out. ¹⁰ ___ the repair man doesn't bring my computer back soon, I'll go crazy!

1	a took ✓	b has taken	c has been taking
2	a am living	b live	c have been living
3	a at	b for	c after
4	a repairs	b is repairing	c is being repaired
5	a on	b by	c through
6	a watch	b have watched	c have been watching
7	a pierced my nose	b been piercing my nose	c had my nose pierced
8	a will play	b would play	c played
9	a out	b off	c over
10	a if	b when	c unless

self-assessment test 4

Vocabulary & Grammar

1 Match the adjectives 1–8 with the correct nouns a–h.

1 sour
2 annoying
3 savoury
4 tender
5 ground
6 grated
7 boiled
8 detached

a cheese
b potatoes
c noises
d snack
e cream
f chicken
g house
h floor

/7

2 Complete the sentences with one letter in each gap.

1 Add the egg, then _pour_ in the milk and mix.
2 Heat the dish in the oven and _ _ _ _ _ it immediately while it's still hot.
3 They live in a three-storey apartment _ _ _ _ _ .
4 Bake the pizza until the cheese _ _ _ _ _ and is golden.
5 A large _ _ _ _ _ room under the roof is ideal for keeping boxes of old books and clothes.
6 Wash the potatoes, then _ _ _ _ them and slice very thinly.
7 She loves sitting on the _ _ _ _ _ _ _ of her flat overlooking the sea.

/6

3 Rewrite the sentences using *have something done*. Don't change the tense used in the original sentence.

1 An optician is testing her eyes.
  She is having her eyes tested.
2 A doctor is going to check Peter's heart.
  _____
3 They have installed a new sink in our kitchen.
  _____
4 Somebody should dye your hair.
  _____
5 A locksmith will change all the locks in my house.
  _____
6 They deliver milk to my aunt's house every day.
  _____

/5

4 Complete the sentences with the correct form of the verbs from the box.

> not make   not borrow ✓   not feel
> knock   lose   let   not nag

1 I wish my younger sister _wouldn't borrow_ my clothes without asking.
2 If she _____ some weight, she'd look really attractive.
3 I wish my parents _____ on the door before coming into my room.
4 If you _____ me to wash up after breakfast, I wouldn't be late for school every day.
5 I _____ you use my computer if you were nicer to me.
6 Mum wishes my younger brother _____ _____ a mess in his bedroom.
7 I wish I _____ sick every time I travel by bus.

/6

5 Complete the second sentence so that it has a similar meaning to the first.

1 Steven Spielberg directed *Schindler's List*.
  Schindler's List _was directed by Steven Spielberg._
2 They are still repairing our car.
  Our car _____ .
3 I'm not happy that I'm so short.
  I wish _____ .
4 People speak English in many countries.
  English _____ .
5 Robert wants to go on holiday to Africa but he hasn't got enough money.
  If Robert _____
  _____ .
6 Somebody has broken three windows in our school.
  Three windows _____ .
7 Auguste and Louis Lumière invented colour photography.
  Colour photography _____
  _____ .

/6

Communication

6 <u>Underline</u> the correct words in the first line of each dialogue. Then choose the second line from options a–e below.

1 A: <u>*Could*</u>/*May* you help me carry the suitcase?

   B: *b*

2 A: Shall *I/you* open the window?

   B: ___

3 A: Would you *mind/want* turning off the radio?

   B: ___

4 A: What's it *made/done* of?

   B: ___

5 A: *What/How* does it taste like?

   B: ___

a Sure, no problem.
b Yes, all right.
c The main ingredients are eggs and milk.
d Yes, please.
e It's very spicy.

/8

7 Complete the dialogue about Paul's house with one word in each gap.

Interviewer: What ^{1} <u>*kind*</u> of house is your parents' house?

Paul: It's a two-storey house in a very good location. It's quite small but I couldn't live anywhere else.

Interviewer: Why do you like it so much?

Paul: There are several ^{2} _____ why I love living there. It's close to my office and it only takes me five minutes to walk there. And I have my own room on the first ^{3} _____ . It's tiny but just right for me.

Interviewer: Is ^{4} _____ a park near your house?

Paul: Yes, and our balcony ^{5} _____ it. I love sitting there in the summer. It's so relaxing. On the other ^{6} _____ it can be quite noisy when kids from the nearby school are playing games during their lunch break.

Interviewer: I see. Are your parents planning to move to a bigger house one day?

Paul: No, I don't think so. In my ^{7} _____ the house size doesn't really matter as long as you feel happy there.

/6

Reading

8 Read the article about sharing accommodation. Match the headings A–G to the paragraphs 1–6. There is one extra heading.

Starting university?

First time living away from home?
Sharing accommodation with other students?
Here are some tips for successful house sharing.

1 ___

Living with other people can be difficult, whether your housemates are close friends or people you hardly know. Don't choose a housemate just because they're great fun. Think about day-to-day living. Will they pay their share of the rent on time? Will they get on with your friends? If you decide to share with someone you hardly know, always ask for personal references first.

2 ___

Establish the rules early – is it okay to borrow clothes, use someone else's phone or personal computer? Always ask before you borrow anything from a housemate, and make sure you take good care of it.

3 ___

If any of your housemates are good cooks and you're not, let them cook and you do the dishes. It may be a good idea to set up a schedule for household tasks, taking turns to clean the bathroom, etc.

4 ___

Try to agree on a minimum standard of cleanliness that you can all stick to. You don't have to be a 'neat freak', but don't leave dirty dishes in the sink or make a mess all over the bedroom, especially if you're sharing with a roommate.

5 ___

Different people have different ideas about day-to-day living. You can't ask your housemates to change themselves if you're not willing to change as well. Listen to what your housemates have to say and find solutions everyone is happy with.

6 ___

Spend time with your housemates and take an interest in what they're doing. Try to find time to be together: maybe just to hang out or to watch a movie. Then you'll get to know your housemates better.

A Be prepared to compromise.
B Respect each other's property.
C Focus on behaviour, not personality.
D Tidy up after yourself.
E Choose your housemates carefully.
F Communicate with each other.
G Divide responsibilities.

/6

Marks

Vocabulary & Grammar	/30 marks
Communication	/14 marks
Reading	/6 marks
Total:	/50 marks

8 help! help!

* easy to do
** a bit harder
*** extra challenge

Vocabulary

Accidents and first aid

1 Match words 1–7 with a–g to make collocations.

1	burn/cut	a	bleeding/swelling
2	sprain	b	head
3	feel	c	painkillers
4	have	d	yourself
5	hit your	e	your ankle
6	stop the	f	dizzy/sick
7	take	g	concussion/a headache

2 Complete the text with the words from the box.

> aid   concussion   burnt   dizzy   feels   headache ✓
> hit   painkiller   plaster   sprains   swelling

SCHOOL NURSE   DISCUSSION

➲ RESEARCH
➲ LIBRARY
➲ BOOKSTORE
➲ BLOGS

Ruby Martin talks about her work as a school nurse

I'm really busy. Kids keep coming all day. Most of the time it's just small things: one girl has a ¹ _headache_ , so I give her a mild ² _____ ; another has cut herself and I put a ³ _____ on the cut. Or a kid ⁴ _____ sick and I give him some mint tea. Sometimes there are injuries from PE lessons. For example, somebody ⁵ _____ their ankle playing football. I put ice on it to stop the ⁶ _____ , and then I usually phone the parents and they take the student home. Once a student ⁷ _____ herself in the science lab. The science teacher gave her first ⁸ _____ by putting her hand under cold water, and then I put a bandage on it. Last month we had a serious incident. A boy ⁹ _____ his head and then he felt sick and ¹⁰ _____ – he had all the symptoms of ¹¹ _____ . I phoned his parents and they took him to hospital. We were all terribly worried, but fortunately it wasn't very bad and he got better after a week.

Grammar

Used to – past continuous

3 (*) Complete the sentences with the correct form of *used to* and the verb in brackets.

1 When I was little, I _used to hate_ (hate) olives.

2 Paul _____ (not/behave) like this before we were married.

3 My granddad _____ (do) a lot of extreme sports when he was younger.

4 _____ (you/go) skiing in winter when you were a child?

5 I _____ (not/go out) as much as I do now.

6 Where _____ (your family/live) before World War II?

4 (**) Underline the correct form to complete the sentences.

1 I always had wonderful holidays as a child. My cousins and I *were playing/used to play* outdoors all day.

2 My grandma *was baking/used to bake* a delicious cake every Saturday.

3 What *were you doing/did you use to do* at seven o'clock yesterday evening?

4 We *were sailing/used to sail* along the coast when suddenly a strong wind threw the boat onto the rocks.

5 Dan *wasn't eating/didn't use to eat* so much when he was younger.

6 The postman came while we *used to have/were having* breakfast.

7 *Were you reading/Did you use to read* a lot as a child?

5 (✲✲) Complete the blog with the correct form (past simple or past continuous) of the verbs in brackets.

⟨ ⟩ C + http://www.partyblog.com ⟨Q· Google⟩

...ed: 28 October   Family parties | Other parties

When I [1] _arrived_ (arrive) at Robert's party last night, Robert and Phil [2] _____ (play) a PlayStation™ game. They [3] _____ (not notice) me at all. Bill and Alice _____ (read) Garfield cartoons. They [5] _____ (offer) to show me the one they [6] _____ (laugh) at. Harry [7] _____ (eat) something as usual. Millie _____ (not/do) anything special, so I [9] _____ (sit) down next to her. While we [10] _____ (talk), ...en more people [11] _____ (arrive). Soon we were all dancing and having a good time.

6 (✲✲✲) **Underline** the correct form to complete the text.

...When I was fourteen, my brother Tim and I [1] _used to be_/ were being crazy about biking. We [2] _were doing_/ ...sed to do tricks on our bikes every afternoon, on a hill ...ear where we lived. We [3] _were seeing/used to see_ a few ...ccidents, but that [4] _didn't stop/didn't use to stop_ us. ...ur mum used to worry about us, but she [5] _believed_/ ...as believing children should have the freedom to ...xperiment. One afternoon we [6] _were riding_/ ...sed to ride up and down the hill as usual. We did a ...ew bunny hops, and then Tim [7] _decided/used to decide_ ...o try and do a front flip. He [8] _landed/was landing_ ...ight on his face with the bike on top of him. He ...used to bleed/was bleeding badly, but he was able to ...tand up. We [10] _rushed/were rushing_ to the local ...ospital. While I phoned our parents, the doctor ... already saw/was already seeing Tim, and so Mum [12] wasn't seeing/didn't see him in the worst state!

Grammar reference

Past simple and past continuous

- The past simple and the past continuous are sometimes used together. The past continuous is used for the action in progress (the background action) and the past simple for the completed action. Sentences like this often use *when*, *while* or *as*:

*Dave and Caroline **were arguing when** I **came** in.*
*He **called while** I **was taking** a shower.*
***As** we **were leaving** the house, I **heard** the phone ring.*

- For completed actions, we normally use the past simple, even if these events happened repeatedly or lasted for a longer time:

*Even if my mum was very angry with my brother, she **tried** (NOT ~~was trying~~) not to shout at him.*

Used to

Form

	+	−
I/You/He/She/ It/We/They	**used to** drink milk.	**did not (didn't) use to** drink milk.

General questions			Short answers		
Did	I/you/he/ she/it/ we/they	**use to** drink milk?	Yes, No,	I/you/he/ she/it/ we/they	**did. didn't.**

Wh-questions

*What did you **use to** drink?*
*Why did you **use to** drink so much milk?*

Use

- We use *used to* to talk about states (*be, have, believe, like*) and actions which happened regularly in the past, but do not happen regularly now:

*I **used to swim** every day.* (I don't do it any more, or I don't do it every day)

- We use *used to*, not the past continuous, to talk about regular past actions:

*I **used to go** (NOT ~~was going~~) abroad every summer.*

- We use the past simple, not *used to*, to talk about something that happened only once:

*I **twisted** (NOT ~~used to twist~~) my ankle in July.* (it happened only once, not regularly)

Vocabulary

Telling a story

1 **Underline** the correct adverbs to complete the story.

Last January, my boyfriend and I were returning from our skiing holiday in Switzerland. We were on a train to Geneva. [1] *Suddenly/Immediately* the train stopped in the middle of a snowy field. [2] *A few minutes later/ At first* a conductor came and explained the train was stuck in the snow. We all got off and walked through deep snow to a nearby village, where we were put in a school building. Some friendly people [3] *finally/ immediately* brought us hot coffee and food. [4] *After that/Meanwhile* we slept in the classrooms. [5] *At first/Meanwhile*, a snow plough arrived and dug out our train. [6] *Eventually/ A few minutes later* we got on the train again and arrived in Geneva the next day. [7] *Fortunately/Unfortunately*, we'd missed our flight home. [8] *At first/In the end*, the airline wanted us to pay the full price of a new ticket. [9] *Fortunately/Unfortunately*, we managed to persuade them that the situation was special and [10] *in the end/suddenly* they put us on the next flight at no extra charge. [11] *Immediately/ Finally*, we arrived home a day late, exhausted but amused by our adventure.

Grammar

Past perfect

2 (✱) **Complete the sentences with the verbs in brackets in the past perfect.**

1 When we finally got to the party, they *'d eaten* (eat) all the birthday cake.

2 Mike was hungry because he _____ (leave) his sandwiches at home.

3 How long _____ (you/know) Steve before you married him?

4 Jessica was nervous because she _____ (never/fly) before.

5 I didn't know who the man was; I _____ (not see) him before.

6 Everything was ready; they _____ (bring) all the equipment the day before.

3 (✱✱) **Complete each sentence with one verb in the past simple and one in the past perfect.**

1 I _felt_ (feel) better after I _had taken_ (take) the painkiller.

2 When Sophie _____ (come) to the party, Nick _____ (already/leave).

3 The rescue teams _____ (arrive) immediately after the accident _____ (happen).

4 I _____ (hear) a lot about John before we _____ (meet).

5 Jack _____ (be) annoyed because he _____ (just/have) an argument with his boss.

6 After we _____ (finish) all the work, we _____ (go) bowling to relax.

4 (✱✱) **Complete the text with the verbs in brackets in the correct form (past simple or past perfect).**

It was 10 p.m. when Julia finally [1] _made_ (make) herself a cup of hot chocolate and [2] _____ (sit) down on the sofa. It [3] _____ (be) a long, tiring day. She [4] _____ (have) eight lessons at school and then she [5] _____ (help) her friend Zoë decorate her room. Now she [6] _____ (feel) really exhausted, but also pleased with herself, because she [7] _____ (never/paint) a room before and she [8] _____ (do) a good job on this one. She [9] _____ (take) a long delicious drink of the hot chocolate and [10] _____ (open) a magazine. She [11] _____ (see) a mobile phone advertisement and suddenly she [12] _____ (remember) something. Oh no! She [13] _____ (leave) her mobile in Zoë's flat!

Grammar plus: reflexive pronouns and *each other*

5 (✱✱) **Complete the sentences with the appropriate reflexive pronouns where necessary. Where no pronoun is needed, write –.**

1 I found it difficult to concentrate
  _–_ in class.

2 I don't think he knows how to
  look after _____ .

3 My younger brother has already
  started to shave _____ .

4 Michelle always dresses
  _____ really beautifully.

5 I cut _____ while slicing the
  tomatoes.

6 At the end of the day, I need
  some quiet time to relax
  _____ .

7 How did you feel _____
  when she said that?

6 (✱✱✱) **Complete the sentences with *each other* or the appropriate reflexive pronoun.**

1 Don't invite Dave and Darren to
  the same party. They really hate
  each other .

2 We didn't enjoy _____ very
  much at the festival.

3 I can't tell you much about him.
  We don't know _____
  very well.

4 Will you stop looking at
  _____ in the mirror and
  listen to me?

5 The two lovers looked adoringly
  at _____ and ignored
  everyone else.

6 The little boy fell off his bike and
  hurt _____ .

7 My little sons fight sometimes
  but they've never really hurt
  _____ .

Grammar reference

Past perfect

Form

We form the past perfect with *had* + past participle of the main verb.

	+	–
I/You/He/She/ It/We/They	**had ('d) gone** to bed.	**had not (hadn't) gone** to bed.

General questions				Short answers		
Had	I/you/he/she/it/ we/they	**gone to** bed?	Yes, No,	I/you/he/she/it/ we/they	**had. hadn't.**

Wh- questions

*How many times **had you seen** Beth before she moved to Spain?*

Use of past perfect

- We use the past perfect to talk about a past event which happened *before* another past event. We use the past simple for the later, main event:

*On the way to the airport I **remembered** that I **had left** my passport at home.* (the second event happened before the first = first I left my passport, then I remembered)

- When we use the past simple and past perfect in one sentence to talk about two past events, we often combine the two clauses with *when, just, already, recently, before* or *after*:

*He **was** very sleepy because **he'd just got out of** bed.*
*I **didn't offer** them anything to eat because they **had already** had dinner.*

Reflexive pronouns and *each other*

Form

	Singular	Plural
1st person (*I, we*)	*myself*	*ourselves*
2nd person (*you*)	*yourself*	*yourselves*
3rd person (*he, she, it, they*)	*himself/herself/itself*	*themselves*

Use of reflexive pronouns

- We use reflexive pronouns to talk about actions where the subject and object are the same person or thing:

*Tom cut **himself** while he was making breakfast.*
*Don't jump into water, boys! You can hurt **yourselves**.*

- We often use reflexive pronouns with verbs such as *cut, hurt, enjoy, look after*:

*They are old enough **to look after themselves**.*

- Some verbs are reflexive in many languages but <u>not</u> in English (for example, *wash, dress, shave, feel, relax, concentrate*).

Use of *each other*

- We use *each other* to talk about actions or feelings which go in both directions between two people:

*Ian doesn't like Mike, and Mike doesn't like Ian. They don't like **each other**.*

- We often use *each other* with verbs such as *love, hate, like, (get to) know, see*:

*I love my younger sister, she loves me too. We love **each other**.*

9

Vocabulary

Arctic exploration

1 Complete the text with the words from the box. There are two extra words.

> abandon expedition ✓
> got stuck sank rescued
> remote crew wave
> exceptional lifeboats

Robert McClure: Arctic explorer

In 1850 an [1] _expedition_ , led by Robert McClure, set out to explore the north part of the Arctic. In early 1853, the expedition ship [2] _____ in the ice and couldn't move. Finally, they had to [3] _____ the ship and climb onto the ice. Soon, the ice destroyed the ship and it [4] _____ . They couldn't use the [5] _____ because the water was completely frozen. McClure and the rest of the [6] _____ had to cross the ice by sledge. The journey was terrible because the men had to march across the ice and soon the situation was getting desperate. They were in a [7] _____ part of the world, far from any towns. Luckily, the men were [8] _____ by another ship, HMS Resolute. McClure and his men became famous. The British Government rewarded them £10,000 and they received gold medals from the British and French geographical societies.

Grace Darling

The first media celebrity?

Today, with so many TV reality programmes and get-famous talent shows, we're used to instant celebrities. In the case of Grace Darling, things were different. Grace was born in Britain in 1815, and of course, there were no cameras, no TV and no internet then. [1] ___ Artists painted her, poets wrote about her. Grace received hundreds of letters, including one from the Queen with a £50 reward (worth about 45,000 euros today). A museum was later established to celebrate her life. Grace was the daughter of a lighthouse keeper, and lived with her family on a remote island off the north-east coast of England – so how did she become so famous?

Reading

2 Look at the picture and the paragraph headings in the text above. Choose the best answers.

1 The text is
   a a newspaper article about different famous people.
   b a biography about a famous person in the past.
   c an article about a woman who became very famous.

2 The woman in the text
   a was rescued from a boat.
   b helped to rescue some people.
   c wanted to rescue some people but couldn't.

3 Read the text and match five of the sentences a–f to the gaps 1–5 in the text. There is one extra sentence.

a On 5 September 1838 the ship *Forfarshire* left Hull to travel to Dundee with about sixty crew plus some passengers.

b Millions of people have visited the Grace Darling Museum.

c People everywhere were amazed by Grace's bravery and praised her heroism.

d But Grace became an international celebrity.

e It was a difficult time for Grace and her family.

f Then she saw survivors on the rocks.

The rescue

___ On 7 September there was a terrible storm and about 4 a.m., when most of the people on board were sleeping, the ship hit rocks. Within fifteen minutes it had broken in two and sunk. Later that morning, Grace was looking out of her window when she saw the wreck. [3] ___ Her father, William Darling, knew that a lifeboat couldn't leave the nearest town because of the storm. He decided to go and help and twenty-two year-old Grace went with him. Together, they rowed over 1.5km through the huge waves and managed to reach the nine survivors. Grace had to row the boat herself while her father leapt out of the boat onto the rocks. One of the survivors was badly hurt, but they managed to rescue them all.

The legend

News of the dramatic rescue appeared in first the local and then the national newspapers – and the legend of Grace Darling was born. [4] ___ Soon Grace was celebrated internationally and received many awards, including the RNLI's* silver medal for bravery.

Royal National Lifeboat Institution, a charity that raises money to buy lifeboats and pay for people to use them.

In the right place at the right time

Grace, an otherwise ordinary young woman, captured the public's imagination. Suddenly, she became the 'ideal woman' in Victorian England – some people wanted to paint her, others wanted souvenirs such as locks of her hair, others wanted to read about her or see her. [5] ___ Sadly, she became ill and died in 1842, aged only twenty-seven.

4 Answer the questions with up to three words.

1 When was Grace born?

_____

2 Which famous person sent a reward to Grace?

_____

3 How much is the reward worth today?

_____

4 What time did the ship sink?

_____

5 How far did Grace and her father row?

_____

6 What award did the RNLI give Grace?

_____

7 How old was Grace when she died?

_____

Listening

5 (17) Listen carefully to four short recordings about the explorer Ernest Shackleton and order the text types.

1 ☐ a description of a film

2 ☐ a presentation

3 ☐ a recorded message

4 ☐ an extract from an interview

6 (17) Listen again. Tick (✓) true or cross (X) false.

1 ☐ The museum is not open on Sundays.

2 ☐ A ticket for a student costs £6.50.

3 ☐ Shackleton was born in England in 1874.

4 ☐ In 1899 Shackleton qualified to command British ships anywhere in the world.

5 ☐ The production team for the film went on three expeditions to the Antarctic.

6 ☐ You can see the original photos from the Shackleton expedition in the film.

7 ☐ Leonard Hussey was allowed to keep his banjo because Shackleton liked music.

8 ☐ On the journey to South Georgia the men had some food every four hours.

Writing

A narrative

1 In **paragraph 1**, set the context for the narrative – give information about *where* and *when* it happened and *who* is involved.

2 Use time expressions to make it clear when the action took place: *Last week, three years ago, at midnight last night*, etc.

3 In **paragraphs 2 and 3**, describe the main events, say *what* happened and *why*.

The best day of my life!

Something wonderful happened last Saturday. I love sports and I'm in the athletics team at school. Last Saturday was the finals of the Sports Championship in our region and I was taking part in the 1000m race. I got up very early and my parents went with me to the sports stadium.

I waited nervously. Finally, it was time for my race. Everything started well and I was in the first three runners. Maybe I could win! We had just started on the last 100m when I fell over! I didn't get up immediately because everyone in the stadium was shouting loudly – I thought they were shouting at me. Luckily, I wasn't badly hurt. I wanted to run away because I felt so embarrassed, but then I decided to get up and finish the race. My heart was beating hard and I didn't think I could win. I ran extremely fast, but in the end I finished in fourth place. I was very disappointed.

After the race, I got changed slowly. Eventually, I went outside. Suddenly, a woman came up to me. She explained that she was looking for talented young athletes and that she was impressed by my speed and determination. She invited me to go to a special sports school where I'll get extra training. I was really excited! Meanwhile, my parents were worried about me. When I told them my news they were happy. Even though I didn't win my race, it was the best day of my life!

4 Use exclamation marks to emphasi[] important information.

5 Describe your feelings.

6 Use sequencing words and adverb[] to show the order [] events: *in the end, immediately, eventually … .*

7 Try to finish your essay in a dramati[] way: *I'll never forget … because … It was t[] best/worst/most frightening/most exciting day/night [] my life!*

1 A good narrative gives lots of information. Read the story above quickly and answer the questions.

1 Who is the story about? _____

2 Where did Julia go? _____

3 When did Julia go there? _____

4 Why didn't Julia win the race? _____

5 What did the woman invite Julia to do?

_____

6 How did Julia feel …

a after the race? _____

b after speaking to the woman? _____

2 Look at the sentences 1–4 from the story and choose the sentence, a or b, which has the same meaning.

1 I didn't get up <u>immediately</u>
a I didn't get up slowly.
b I didn't get up at once.

2 <u>Eventually</u>, I went outside.
a After a short time I went outside.
b After a long time I went outside.

3 <u>Suddenly</u>, a woman came up to me.
a A woman came up to me slowly.
b A woman came up to me quickly and unexpectedly.

4 <u>Meanwhile</u>, my parents were worried about me.
a My parents were worrying about me during this time.
b My parents worried about me for a short time.

3 Underline the correct words to complete the text.

Posted: 28 October

I was sitting at home last Saturday morning when the phone ¹ *eventually/suddenly* rang. It was my friend John – he had a spare ticket for a Leona Lewis concert that evening! I love her music, so I was very excited. We decided to meet at the concert hall. I waited for twenty minutes, but John didn't appear. ² *Eventually/Immediately* I discovered he was waiting for me at one door. ³ *Meanwhile/Immediately* I was waiting for him at another door. What a disaster! Finally, we went inside. At first, we stayed at the back, but after that we went down to the front. ⁴ *Suddenly/Eventually* Leona started to shake people's hands. I ⁵ *immediately/meanwhile* tried to get near her. Then I waited – would she shake my hand? ⁶ *Eventually/Immediately* she reached me and shook my hand! It was the best evening of my life!

Simon

4 Complete the strategies box with the words below.

> events   word order   narrative ✓   sequencing

A narrative

- Read the task carefully. Think about what interesting information you can include in your ¹ *narrative* and make notes.
- Think about the *wh-* words to help you set the context and describe the main ² _____ : *who, what, where, when, what happened, how the person felt*.
- Organise your notes into paragraphs and write the first version.
- Read your narrative and think what you can do to make it more interesting – add exclamation marks, adjectives, ³ _____ words and adverbs.
- Check the number of words and then check your ⁴ _____ , grammar and punctuation.

5 Choose one of the tasks and write your narrative. Use the strategies in exercise 4 to help you. Write 200–250 words.

> Write about:
>
> 1 A surprising event that happened to you or someone you know. Finish the narrative with the words *It was the best day of my life!*
>
> 2 Imagine you are Julia's mother and rewrite her story from your point of view.

Speaking

Making arrangements

6 Choose the best phrase for each situation.

> That would be great!
> How about going to see a film?
> What are you doing at the weekend?
> I'd love to, but I have plans.
> Do you fancy going to a party?
> What's new?

1 You want to start a conversation.
   What's new?

2 You want to invite someone to go to the cinema.
   _____

3 Someone has invited you out, but you can't go.
   _____

4 Someone has invited you out and you can go.
   _____

5 You want to know about someone's plans.
   _____

6 You want to invite someone to a party.
   _____

7 Use the prompts to write invitations in the dialogues. Then accept (✓) or refuse (✗) the offers with a reason. Use as many different expressions as you can.

1 go/shopping/after school?
   A: *Do you fancy going shopping after school?*
   B: (✗) *I'm sorry, I can't. I've got a guitar lesson.*

2 go/to the sports centre/on Saturday?
   A: _____
   B: (✓) _____

3 meet/for a coffee/tomorrow?
   A: _____
   B: (✗) _____

4 go/to an art exhibition/on Sunday?
   A: _____
   B: (✗) _____

5 watch/a film on TV/tonight
   A: _____
   B: (✓) _____

help! help!

10 in the news

*	easy to do
**	a bit harder
***	extra challenge

Vocabulary

Newspapers

1 Rearrange the letters to make words or phrases found in newspapers. The first and last letters are in the correct position.

a anesirevdemt   _advertisement_

b cotoran   _____

c flim riveew   _____

d gisosp cumoln   _____

e hamun itresnet sroty   _____

f hprosocoe   _____

g lteter to the etodir   _____

h nwes alirtce   _____

i sprots nwes   _____

2 What kinds of texts are the following? Match texts 1–7 with seven of the words a–i from exercise 1.

1 ☑ **Who Is Miss World's Mysterious New Boyfriend?**

2 ☐ **Barack Obama meets with G20 leaders in Pittsburgh**

3 ☐ *Sir,*
I was shocked to read your article on the proposed changes to our education system.

4 ☐ **LIVERPOOL SIGN UP NEW GOALKEEPER**

5 ☐ You've got to ask yourself how this banal romantic comedy got to win three Academy Awards. The plot is predictable, the acting weak and

6 ☐ **Homeless teen becomes a top student**

7 ☐ **Aquarius** (20 January – 18 February) Allow your feelings to guide you this week. The Moon influences your ruling planet

Grammar

Reported speech

3 (*) Complete the second sentence with the correct pronouns.

1 'I don't want to upset my mother,' said Sylvia.
Sylvia said _she_ didn't want to upset _her_ mother.

2 George said, 'I'm going to visit my friends on Saturday.'
George said _____ was going to visit _____ friends on Saturday.

3 John and Claire said, 'We took our children to the zoo.'
John and Claire said _____'d taken _____ children to the zoo.

4 'I talked to your sister about the trip,' Sam told me.
Sam said _____'d talked to _____ sister about the trip.

5 I told Joe, 'I discussed the trip with your cousin.'
I told Joe _____'d discussed the trip with _____ cousin.

4 (**) Read Mike's holiday blog, then complete what Bob said in direct speech.

The Blog Site

This is a photo of Bob, a Scottish guy I met in France last summer. He told me (1) he was cycling across Europe. He said (2) he'd just come from Brussels, and (3) before that he'd cycled all the way from Aberdeen. He explained (4) he didn't like cars or buses. He told me (5) he was going to Sicily, and (6) when the holiday was over, he and his bike would return home by train.

1 _'I'm cycling across Europe.'_

2 'I _____ Brussels.'

3 'Before that, I _____ from Aberdeen.'

4 'I _____ cars or buses.'

5 'I _____ Sicily.'

6 'When the holiday _____ over, my bike and I _____ home by train.'

5 **(✶✶)** Read what Bob said when he phoned Mike on his return, and complete Mike's blog using reported speech.

> *The rest of the trip was wonderful. I didn't get as far as Sicily in the end; I stayed in southern Italy. I'm writing an article about my trip. I've almost finished it. Some day I'll cycle to India!*

Blog Site

Got a phone call from Bob, the Scottish cyclist, today. He told me the rest of his trip [1] _had been_ wonderful. He said _____ as far as Sicily in the end; he [3] _____ in southern Italy. He added he [4] _____ an article about his trip and he [5] _____ it. Finally, he told me some day that he [6] _____ India.

6 **(✶✶)** When Bob was setting off on his next trip, his mother asked him to remember a few important things. Rewrite what she said in reported speech.

1 'Clean your teeth regularly!'
She told _him to clean his teeth regularly_ .

2 'Wash your socks every day.'
She told _____ .

3 'Keep your passport in a safe place!'
She told _____ .

4 'Please text me every day.'
She asked _____ .

5 'Please send a postcard to your grandma.'
She asked _____ .

Grammar plus: Time expressions in reported speech

7 **(✶✶✶)** Complete the sentences to report what the people said. Make all the necessary changes and remember to change the time expressions in bold.

1 'School finishes **today**.'
He said _school finished that day_ .

2 'We're going to Spain **tomorrow**.'
They said _____ .

3 'We packed all our luggage **yesterday**.'
They said _____ .

4 'We'll be back **next month**.'
They said _____ .

5 'We travelled all around South America **last year**.'
They said _____ .

6 'I haven't got a full-time job **now**.'
He said _____ .

Grammar reference

Reported speech

When we tell others what someone has said, we can quote their words directly (direct speech) or report them indirectly (reported speech).

- In direct speech, we give the person's exact words:
'The film was very interesting.' → She said 'The film was very interesting.'

- In reported speech, we explain what the person said without giving their exact words. We normally make changes to verb tenses, pronouns and time and place expressions:

Form

Direct speech	Reported speech
Present simple 'I **don't like** football.'	**Past simple** Dave said (that) he **didn't like** football.
Present continuous 'I **am going** to the cinema.'	**Past continuous** Dave said (that) he **was going** to the cinema.
Present perfect 'Tom **has failed** his driving test.'	**Past perfect** Dave said (that) Tom **had failed** his driving test.
Past simple 'My sister **didn't tell** me the truth.'	**Past perfect** Dave said (that) his sister **hadn't told** him the truth.
will 'I hope it **won't** happen again.'	*would* Dave said (that) he hoped it **wouldn't happen** again.

Pronouns

*'I don't need **your** help, I can open the tin **myself**.'* → He told me (that) **he** didn't need **my** help and that **he** could open the tin **himself**.
*'I know **you** haven't baked the cake **yourself**.'* → My girlfriend said (that) **she** knew I hadn't baked the cake **myself**.

Time and place expressions

now → *at that time/then   today* → *that day*
tomorrow → *the next day/the following day*
in three days' time → *three days later*
next week → *the following week*
yesterday → *the day before/the previous day*
four hours ago → *four hours earlier/four hours before*
last week → *the week before/the previous week*
here → *there   this* → *that, the*

*'I left it **here yesterday**.'* → He told me (that) he had left it **there the day before/the previous day.**

Reported orders

When we report a request or command, we often use the structure: *ask/tell/order someone to/not to* + infinitive:

'Listen carefully to the instructions.' → The teacher **asked us to listen** carefully to the instructions.

10

Vocabulary
Celebrities and the media

1 Match 1–5 with a–e to make collocations.

1 print   a pressure
2 behave   b attention
3 be under   c an influence on
4 desperate for   d lies
5 have   e badly

2 Read the news item. Then match the beginnings 1–7 with the endings of the comments a–g below.

REAL LIFE NEWS   ✕

Home | UK | World | Business | Technology | Science | **Sport** | Entertainment
Headlines | Olympic Games | **Football** | Cricket | Rugby Union | Rugby League | Snooke

FOOTBALL NEWS

Footballer Johnny Thomas, arrested in October after he'd attacked a man in a nightclub, was sentenced to two months in prison yesterday. This means he will miss the UEFA European Football Championships.

1 A very good decision!
2 I don't believe Johnny did that.
3 He's always been desperate for attention, hasn't he?
4 Why don't the media leave him alone?
5 I'm sorry for him. I think the punishment is too hard.
6 I don't worry about Mr Thomas. What worries me is the effect of his behaviour on others.
7 I don't believe young people are influenced by anyone's example.

a He should have the right to some privacy!
b He behaved badly and he got what he deserved.
c He's probably been under a lot of pressure recently because of the championships and that's why he did it.
d Newspapers are always printing lies about him.
e They're much too self-centred for that.
f Think about the influence his example may have young people.
g Well, now he's certainly got all the publicity he wants.

Grammar
Reported questions

3 (✳) Complete the reported questions by putting the words in brackets in the correct order.

1 'Do you live in Manchester?'
He wanted to know if _I lived in Manchester_ (Manchester/I/in/lived).

2 'Did you see Tom earlier?'
Mary asked if _____ _____ (seen/I/had/Tom) earlier.

3 'What are you thinking about?'
She wanted to know what _____ _____ (about/thinking/I/was).

4 'What are you going to do on Sunday?'
Daniel asked what _____ _____ (going/were/to/we/do) on Sunday.

5 'Why have all the guests left?'
Kate wondered why _____ _____ (the/left/all/had/guests).

6 'Where is the Royal Palace?'
The tourist asked _____ _____ (was/where/the/Palace/Royal)

4 (✳✳) Rachel applied for a job with a newspaper. After the interview, she told her friend about the questions she was asked. Complete what Rachel said in reported speech.

1 'Have you worked in the media before?'
She asked (me) _if I'd worked in the media before_ .

2 'Have you done much writing?'
She asked _____ _____ .

3 'What sort of texts have you written?'
She wanted to know _____ _____ .

4 'What languages do you speak?'
She asked _____ _____ .

5 'Where did you learn Spanish?'
She wanted to know _____ _____ .

6 'Are you available seven days a week?'
She wanted to know _____ _____ .

7 'Will it be a problem for you to have your mobile on all the time?'
She asked _____ _____ .

5 **(**)** Rachel also asked the interviewer some questions. Below is what she later said to her friend. Write the questions she asked in direct speech.

1 I asked if I'd get some sort of training.

   Will I get some sort of training?

2 I asked how much I'd earn.

   How much _____ ?

3 I asked if she'd read my article on student rights.

   _____ ?

4 I asked how many days of holidays their employees got per year.

   How many days of holidays _____ ?

5 I asked if they had a staff canteen.

   _____ ?

6 **(***)** Complete the reported questions, making all the necessary changes.

1 Do you live here?

   I asked the girl *if she lived there* .

2 Where were you yesterday?

   The teacher asked me _____ .

3 What are you working on now?

   The interviewer asked the artist _____ .

4 What are we going to do tomorrow?

   My girlfriend wondered _____ .

5 Where did you live six months ago?

   The policeman asked the man _____ .

6 Have you seen this article?

   My friend asked me _____ .

7 Where do you think you'll be in five years' time?

   Charlie asked Mike _____ .

Grammar reference

Reported questions

Word order in reported questions

- When we report questions, we use the same word order as in reported statements (the subject comes before the verb).
- We change the same elements as in reported statements (verb tenses, pronouns, time and place expressions).
- When we report questions, we often use *ask*, *wonder*, *want to know*:

*'**Are you going** home?'* (direct question)
*He asked if **I was going** home.* (reported question – the subject comes before the verb)
*'**Do you like** flowers?'* (direct question)
*He wanted to know if **I liked** flowers.* (reported question – no auxiliary verb *do*)

Reporting *yes/no* questions

- When we report *yes/no* questions, we use *if* or *whether*:

'Do you want to take a rest?' → *He asked **if/whether** I wanted to take a rest.*
'Did you have a good time at the party?' → *Pete wanted to know **if/whether** we had had a good time at the party.*

Reporting *wh-* questions

- When we report *wh-* questions, we use *ask* + the same question word (*what, who, how, where, when,* etc.) as in the original question:

*'**Why** have you come so late?'* → *He asked me **why** I had come so late.*
*'**When** will I see them again?'* → *She wondered **when** she would see them again.*

Vocabulary

Crime

1 Complete the text with the best words, a, b or c in each gap.

> ✕
>
> ### Welcome to the online police forum
>
> #### What should we do about crime?
>
> Every year the number of people who ¹ _a_ crimes
> increases. If thieves ² ___ your house or they ³ ___ a lot
> of money, how should they be punished? Should they
> pay a ⁴ ___ or get a prison ⁵ ___ ? Most people agree
> criminals should ⁶ ___ prison for serious crimes, but
> what about less serious crimes? What should we do?
> For example, some teenage boys ⁷ ___ out of control
> and do some damage to a school or other building.
> Should they ⁸ ___ the damage with their own money?
> Will they ⁹ ___ their lesson from this? And what about
> people who ¹⁰ ___ into computers? What do you think?
> Write and tell us!

1 a commit ✓	**b** do	**c** make
2 a steal	**b** break into	**c** go to
3 a catch	**b** damage	**c** steal
4 a call	**b** fine	**c** prosecutor
5 a fine	**b** time	**c** sentence
6 a stay	**b** go to	**c** have
7 a go	**b** make	**c** get
8 a pay	**b** pay for	**c** pay back
9 a take	**b** study	**c** learn
10 a hack	**b** break	**c** play

2 Complete the text with the correct form of the words in brackets.

What happens if I am arrested?

⊙ *The police will explain the reason for your*
¹ _arrest_ *(arrest) and charge you with a*
² _____ *(criminal).*

⊙ *You should contact a* ³ _____ *(law) as
soon as possible and talk to him or her about
your case. You need a* ⁴ _____ *(defend)
lawyer to defend you.*

⊙ *When the case goes to court, the*
⁵ _____ *(prosecute) will explain the
case against you.*

⊙ *The judge will decide your* ⁶ _____
(punish) – it might simply be a ⁷ _____
(fine) or it might be more serious.

Reading

3 Read the dictionary extracts below. Then look at the photo and the paragraph headings. What do you think the text will be about?

> **affect** *v* to change or influence something

> **demand** *n* wanted by a lot of people

> **harass** *v* to behave in an unpleasant or threatening way towards someone

> **pose [for a picture]** *v* to sit or stand so that someone can take a photo of you

> **publicity** *n* attention in the media

4 Read the text and choose the best summary.

1 The text is about how to take photographs of famous people.

2 The text explains why famous people don't like paparazzi photographers.

3 The text is about why ordinary people like looking at photos of famous people.

5 Read the text and choose the correct answers.

1 According to the text, one of the difficult things about being famous is
   a you are always stressed about something.
   b you get bad publicity all the time from the media.
   c your life is no longer private.
   d there is a lot of pressure to tell people about your life.

2 There are more paparazzi now because
   a most photographers think it is a very glamorous job.
   b there are more magazines and newspapers that want their photos.
   c all magazines want to publish their photos these days.
   d more celebrities behave badly now than before.

3 Lisa Michaels
   a doesn't often read about her favourite celebrities.
   b is a teenager who is famous for taking photos of stars.
   c doesn't understand why magazinesabout stars are so popular.
   d thinks celebrities should expect to be photographed.

4 According to Norman Newman,
   a readers expect newspapers to have stories about celebrity scandals.
   b people only want to know about the bad behaviour of celebrities.
   c everyone knows what stars look like without make-up.
   d people don't want posed photos at all nowadays.

5 Robert Pattinson wants to avoid the paparazzi because
   a he has just been in prison.
   b they take photos of his friends.
   c he can't keep in touch with his fans.
   d they have threatened his security guard.

6 ___ went to court because paparazzi photographers chased him/her and caused a car crash.
   a Sienna Miller
   b Lily Allen
   c Amy Winehouse
   d Mark Thomson

6 **Read the text and answer the questions with up to three words.**

1 According to the media, what kind of stories do people enjoy reading?

_____

2 Which internet sites for blogs and posts are mentioned?

_____

3 What do celebrities complain they can't do because of the paparazzi?

_____

4 Who is Robert Pattinson?

_____

5 Is Lily Allen happy about the result of her court case?

_____

The price of fame?

Being famous has disadvantages. Stars lose their privacy and are affected by negative publicity – and this is very stressful. The growing number of magazines and newspapers that publish stories about the private lives of celebrities means there are more paparazzi* now.

Celebrities accuse the media of harassing them and spreading gossip. The media say everyone loves human interest stories. Appearing in the press, they say, is the price of fame.

'We want to see photos'

'Famous people know they will be photographed; it's part of being a celebrity,' says teenager Lisa Michaels.

'Everyone wants to read about their favourite celebrities and see photos of them. That's why magazines and newspapers that publish them are so popular.'

Previously, people were happy to see posed photographs of the stars. However, today we have reality TV and the internet. People write about their private lives in blogs and posts on Facebook, MySpace or Twitter. What is 'public' and what is 'private' is no longer so clear. 'Nowadays,' says sociologist Norman Newman, 'we want to know what the stars look like without make-up, or when they are behaving badly. People

expect to read about scandals, not just read news articles – and they want to see the photos.'

'It's a nightmare'

However, many celebrities complain that because of the paparazzi they can never relax. For some people, it can get so bad it affects their health and quality of life. Actor Robert Pattinson, star of the Twilight films, worries about his security. 'It's a nightmare,' he says. 'I haven't been able to meet friends because I know photographers will be waiting. I can't even talk to my fans because the photographers follow me everywhere.' He feels he has become a 'prisoner' of the paparazzi.

Now, more and more celebrities are protecting themselves against the paparazzi. Recently actress Sienna Miller and singers Amy Winehouse and Lily Allen won court cases to stop press agencies from sending paparazzi to photograph them. Lily Allen was in a car accident after she was chased by a photographer. Allen's lawyer, Mark Thomson, said: My client has been harassed over the last few months by the paparazzi. The court has forbidden paparazzi photographers to take photos. She is delighted.'

* The paparazzi are photographers who take photos of celebrities when they do not expect to be photographed – for example, when they go shopping, walk through the city, eat at a restaurant or go on holiday.

Reading

Gapped text

1 Read the text. Look at the <u>underlined</u> words and answer the questions.

> Alice decided to visit her boyfriend in Scotland at the weekend. <u>She</u> left home on Saturday morning, got into her car and set off. <u>After a few hours</u> the car suddenly stopped on the motorway. <u>It</u> had run out of fuel. There was no petrol station nearby, <u>so</u> Alice decided to phone for help.

1 Who is 'She'? _____

2 'After a few hours' means a few hours after she

_____

3 What is 'It'? _____

4 Alice decided to phone for help because

_____

2 Read the first part of a newspaper article about a crash landing. Three sentences have been taken out of the text. Match the sentences a–c below to gaps 1–3. The <u>underlined</u> words will help you.

'The Miracle on the Hudson'

How one pilot's skill saved 155 lives

On 15 January, 2009 an Airbus A320 with 155 people on board took off from New York's La Guardia airport. [1] ___
'I heard an explosion, and I saw flames coming from the left wing, and I thought, "this isn't good",' remembers one of the passengers.
Planes often collide with birds. [2] ___
Captain Chesley Sullenberger found himself in charge of a plane with no engines, at an altitude of just over 900 metres over New York City. [3] ___

a <u>He</u> prepared to land on the Hudson River, between Manhattan and New Jersey.

b <u>A few minutes later</u>, two Canada geese – large water birds – hit both of <u>its</u> engines, causing them to fail immediately.

c <u>But</u> accidents which seriously damage the aircraft are unusual, and a 'double strike' like this is incredibly rare.

Exam Tip

The following kinds of words show you the connections in the text and can help you match sentences to gaps:

• pronouns, e.g. *he, his, they, them*
• time expressions, e.g. *after that, a few minutes later*
• linking words, e.g. *but, so, because*

3 Read the rest of the article. Four sentences have been taken out of the text. Match the sentences a–e below to gaps 1–4. There is one extra sentence.

To land safely on water, a pilot must first reduce speed as much as possible, so that the plane doesn't break into pieces the moment it touches the water. [1] ___ All of this is very difficult to do without engines. New Yorkers working in nearby office buildings watched the Airbus land smoothly on the river, 'like on a runway'.
The plane immediately started filling with ice-cold water, but the crew kept the situation under control. [2] ___
'They did a wonderful job,' said another passenger.
Rescue teams arrived within minutes. Some people stood on the plane's wings, others jumped or were carried into boats. Some found themselves in water, but were quickly rescued. Captain Sullenberger was the last to leave the sinking plane. [3] ___
Almost miraculously, no-one was killed. Except for one person whose legs were broken, no-one suffered serious injuries. The mayor of New York described the pilot as a hero. [4] ___ It is likely that future pilots will be trained using videos of his Hudson landing.

a He walked its whole length twice, waist-deep in water, to check no-one had been left on board.

b They calmly helped all the passengers to get out of the sinking aircraft.

c At that moment she saw the engine blow up.

d Captain Sullenberger said only, 'This is what we are trained to do.'

e He or she must then make sure the landing is very flat, so the plane doesn't dive into water or roll over.

Listening

Matching

4 (18) Listen to a person talking about herself and the media. What do you think her job is?

5 (18) Listen again and note down at least three words or phrases which helped you to answer the question.

6 (19) Listen to four people talking about themselves and the media. Match the speakers 1–4 to their jobs a–e. There is one extra job.

a ☐ actor
b ☐ artist
c ☐ business person
d ☐ journalist
e ☐ housewife

Use of English

Error correction

7 In each of the sentences below, cross out one word which should not be there.

1 Jack ~~has~~ sprained his ankle yesterday.
2 The man which I talked to seemed very friendly.
3 We discussed about our plans.
4 He asked me where did I lived.
5 The article was a very interesting.
6 Finally I could relax myself.
7 The sailors have been abandoned the ship.
8 My favourite sport is the swimming.

8 Complete the exam tip with examples from exercise 7.

9 Read the text below. In some of the lines there is a word which should not be there. Tick (✓) the correct lines. If a line has a word which should not be there, circle the word.

Our yacht sank after hitting a whale!

1 My wife and I (were) used to dream of sailing
2 around the world for years. Finally last year ✓
3 we had been saved enough money to buy a
4 yacht and we set out on our dream voyage.
5 One day we were sailing from the Jamaica
6 to Puerto Rico when suddenly something
7 massive has hit the boat. It was a whale!
8 The boat started filling with water very quickly.
9 For a moment I felt myself scared, but my wife
10 was a very calm. She took the 'emergency bag'
11 who we always kept ready and we got into a life
12 raft. Soon we were rescued by another yacht.
13 Back home, a reporter asked us what did we
14 planned to do now. I told to him we were hoping
15 to buy another boat soon!

exam trainer 5

Vocabulary & Grammar

1 **Complete the definitions with the correct words.**

1 A medicine which reduces or removes pain –
a _painkiller_.

2 Something wrong with your body which shows
that you have a particular illness – _ _ _ _ _ _ _ .

3 A regular article in a newspaper/magazine
about private lives of famous people –
_ _ _ _ _ _ column.

4 To be unable to stand steadily because you
are ill – to feel _ _ _ _ _ .

5 A funny drawing in a newspaper/magazine,
especially about politicians or events in the
news – _ _ _ _ _ _ _ .

6 All the people who work on a ship or plane –
the _ _ _ _ .

7 An article in a newspaper that gives an
opinion about a new film – a film _ _ _ _ _ _ .

8 All the organisations, such as television, radio,
and newspapers, that provide news and
information for the public – the _ _ _ _ _ .

/7

2 **Use the words in capitals to complete the
second sentence so that it has the same
meaning as the first.**

1 It was his first time in the zoo.   NEVER
He _had never been to the zoo_ before.

2 I don't go to the cinema as often as before.
USED
I _____ often.

3 She entered the room in the middle of my
argument with Tom.   ARGUING
She _____ with Tom.

4 'Put your books away.'   TOLD
My mother _____ away.

5 I felt sick from eating too many cakes.   BECAUSE
I _____ many cakes.

6 He has a habit of sleeping during the day, but
he didn't when he was younger.   DIDN'T
He _____ during the day.

7 Can you help me with my homework?'   ASKED
My brother _____ homework.

/6

3 Underline **the correct words to complete the
sentences.**

1 The doctor put a *plaster/bandage/painkiller*
around my head.

2 I've *cut/hit/burnt* myself while baking despite
wearing oven gloves.

3 Too much attention can be very annoying
at first, but *suddenly/eventually/immediately*
celebrities learn how to live with it.

4 My sprained ankle was quite painful and I couldn't
stop *the bleeding/concussion/the swelling*.

5 I watch *the news/advertisements/the horoscopes*
every day to know what's going on in the world.

6 Many famous people are tired of reporters
following them everywhere and want more
publicity/pressure/privacy.

/5

4 **Complete the sentences with the correct form
of the verbs from the box.**

> meet ✓   have   sink   hurt   get   rescue

1 They _met_ while they were working in Paris.

2 At that moment it became clear that the ship
_____ very fast.

3 I was so happy when I learnt that firefighters
_____ my neighbours from the house fire.

4 His friends _____ a strong influence on
him when he was a teenager.

5 Julia told her teacher that she was late
because she _____ stuck in a traffic jam.

6 The doctor said that my arm _____ for a
short while after the injection.

/5

5 **Correct the mistakes in the sentences.**

1 By the time we got home, ~~they~~ already left.   *they'd*

2 Ian asked me why didn't I come to his party.

3 Beth didn't used to be so sociable.

4 He said me that he wanted to go home.

5 Rob asked us we had plans for the weekend.

6 I told her that Tom and I are going to get married.

7 I took a photo of my sister while she slept.

8 Their teacher asked them stop talking.

/7

Reading

6 Read the article about a sea rescue. Match seven of the phrases a–h to the correct place 1–7 in the text. There is one extra phrase.

Lifeguards rescue teenagers from sea

Three lifeguards were hailed as heroes last night after they rescued dozens of teenagers from the sea. The quick action and bravery of the lifeguards saved several of the youngsters from certain death.

The group of thirty-six youngsters were on an outdoor activity holiday in West Wales. On Saturday afternoon, the group, accompanied by four adults, went down to the sea. Some of them did not know how to swim ¹___ . They were taking part in an exercise to help build confidence and teamwork. As part of the exercise they were walking backwards into the sea. At the time the tide was out and the water was not deep. The tide began to come in and ²___ . Suddenly the sandbank underneath them collapsed and the sea flooded in. Some of the teenagers were soon in dangerous waters.

Fortunately, three Royal National Lifeboat Institution (RNLI) lifeguards ³___ .

Jon Johnson, ⁴___ Adam Pitman and Coral Lewis, said it was 'the biggest rescue I've seen'. He explained that some of the teenagers were having problems because they couldn't swim. Others found it hard because it is difficult to swim with all your clothes on. Some of the group went under the water and ⁵___ . The lifeguards immediately went in with rescue boards.

Two of the group needed to go to hospital, ⁶___ . Jacob Thomas, sixteen, a member of the group, said that at first it was fine. 'We were all in up to about our shoulders and the bank just gave way and the tide kept coming in,' he said. 'Everyone started to panic a little bit.'

David Miller, manager for the local coastguard, said that although the sea was fairly shallow, ⁷___ . 'It is just fortunate that the lifeguards were quickly on the scene and lucky that lives were not lost,' he added.

a who was on duty with colleagues
b thanked them for what they did
c were in danger of drowning
d and had never seen the sea before the trip
e the group started walking back to dry land
f it was still very dangerous in that area
g were nearby and came to the rescue
h both suffering from the effects of the cold water

/3

Listening

7 🔘20 Listen to Kate and Mark's presentation. Read the statements and tick (✓) true or cross (✗) false or write (?) if there is no information.

1 ☐ Kate mentions two talent shows.
2 ☐ Fifteen million people in the UK watch *Britain's Got Talent* every week.
3 ☐ Mark is critical of talent shows.
4 ☐ Michael Jackson used to be Mark's favourite singer.
5 ☐ In his talk, Mark asked the audience to stop laughing at talent show contestants.

/5

Communication

8 Put the questions and answers in the correct order to make a dialogue.

a ☐ Not too bad, thanks. Listen, what are you doing tomorrow? Do you fancy going to the cinema?
b ☐1 Hi, Pete. How are things at school?
c ☐ I'm sorry, I can't. I'm going to London tomorrow. Why don't we go on Monday evening?
d ☐ See you then!
e ☐ Everything's fine. And how are you, Dan?
f ☐ Sounds good. I'll see you on Monday.

/5

9 Complete the dialogue with one word in each gap.

A: What do you ¹*think* about a separate TV set for children's bedrooms?

B: ²P_____ I don't think it's a good idea. I feel ³s_____ for children who spend all the time in front of the telly because their parents don't have time for them.

A: I agree, actually. I think parents ⁴s_____ spend more time with their children instead of buying them new gadgets.

/3

Marks

Vocabulary & Grammar	/30 marks
Reading	/7 marks
Listening	/5 marks
Communication	/8 marks
Total:	/50 marks

✱	easy to do
✱✱	a bit harder
✱✱✱	extra challenge

Vocabulary

Cultural events

1 Match sentences 1–6 with sentences a–f to make continuous speeches.

1 My aunt took me to the opera once.

2 We're putting on a play at school.

3 Did you go to the Mike & The Mob gig last Saturday?

4 They're organising a big rock festival in our town.

5 My boyfriend wants me to go to a classical concert at the weekend.

6 There's a new exhibition on at the gallery of modern art.

a It's a famous orchestra and a great conductor, and he says I must see it.

b The atmosphere was exciting and the audience had a good time, but the backing musicians weren't great.

c You can see some really strange paintings.

d My friend plays one of the main roles, and I'm responsible for the lighting.

e I liked the sets and the costumes, but I hated the music!

f They've invited lots of great bands and they're putting up a huge stage in the market square.

2 Complete the sentences with nouns or adjectives formed from the words in brackets.

1 He's a good songwriter, but not an especially good _performer_ (perform).

2 Have you seen that new _____ (music)? I loved the songs, and the dancing is great.

3 When I was in London I saw an _____ (exhibit) of African art.

4 My cousin is studying at the Royal College of Music; he wants to be a _____ (conduct).

5 There's an _____ (excite) new quiz show on TV.

6 Some of the _____ (back) musicians in that concert were awful.

7 My neighbour is an artist. Right now she's working on a huge new _____ (sculpt).

Grammar

Gerunds and infinitives

3 ✱ Underline the correct form to complete the sentences.

1 I enjoy *to listen/listening* to live music with friends.

2 Phil can't stand *to go/going* to the opera.

3 We agreed *organising/to organise* a concert at the end of the school year.

4 I went to the party especially *to meet/meeting* Emily.

5 It's cheaper *to travel/travelling* by bus than by train.

6 *Going/Go* to six different festivals is Mike's idea of a great holiday.

4 ✱ Why did they do it? Complete each sentence with an infinitive of purpose using the phrases from the box.

> tell her he was okay   see some paintings
> buy tickets for the show
> take photos during the trip ✓
> invite them to a party

1 Sam bought a camera _to take photos during the trip_ .

2 Ella went to the museum _____ .

3 Sophie wrote an email to her friends _____ _____ .

4 Chris phoned his mum _____ .

5 Daniel went to the theatre _____ .

5 ✱✱ Complete the sentences with the correct preposition and the gerund of the verbs in brackets.

1 I'm interested _in applying_ (apply) for a job at the film festival.

2 We were bored _____ (do) the same job every day.

3 The children are very excited _____ (go) to see the musical.

4 I'm fed up _____ (listen) to his complaints.

5 Millie is thinking _____ (become) an actress.

6 I've always dreamed _____ (live) in a hot country.

7 Charlie is very keen _____ (study) photography.

6 (✶✶) Complete the blog with the correct form (gerund or infinitive) of the verbs in brackets.

HOME | BLOGS | CONTACT

we love music

⊙ Posted by Jill on 28 November

My cousin Jack and I have been making music together for years. Last year we wanted ¹ _to get_ (get) our own electric guitars, but we couldn't afford ² _____ (buy) them. We decided ³ _____ (earn) some money.

First, Jack suggested ⁴ _____ (work) at a supermarket. It was easy ⁵ _____ (get) the job, but we really hated ⁶ _____ (sit) at the checkout for hours without a break. Then we worked as waiters in a café. ⁷ _____ (serve) customers was okay, but it was tiring and the money was not so good. And then we had a great idea. We offered ⁸ _____ (play) in the café in the evenings. We did it all summer ⁹ _____ (save) the money we needed.

¹⁰ _____ (perform) in a café can be fun, but on some days we were really fed up with ¹¹ _____ (sing) the same songs all the time. But by September we managed ¹² _____ (save) enough for two really good electric guitars and some equipment.

⊙ Posted by Phil on 28 November

Grammar plus: *want, would like, expect +* infinitive

7 (✶✶✶) Complete the text with the phrases from the box.

> to study   her to study
> someone to succeed   to become ✓
> her brother to become

Problem parents

My friend Vera has got a problem with her parents. She'd like ¹ _to become_ a dancer, but they want ² _____ management. They would also like ³ _____ a lawyer, but he wants ⁴ _____ architecture. How can you expect ⁵ _____ in a career they don't want? Help! What should Vera and Nick do?

Grammar reference

Gerunds and infinitives

Sometimes two verbs in an English sentence follow one other. The first verb can be followed by the gerund or infinitive form of the second:

I **hate swimming**. (*hate* is followed by the gerund *swimming*)

I **want to study** medicine. (*want* is followed by the infinitive *to study*)

Verbs with gerunds

Some verbs are followed by the gerund. Common verbs that take the gerund are:

avoid, can't stand, consider, enjoy, give up, hate, like, love, miss, not mind, practise, prefer, start, stop, suggest

I **suggest going** to the cinema instead of the theatre.

- The gerund can be the object of the sentence:

I prefer **playing football** to watching it on TV.

- The gerund can be the subject of the sentence:

Eating sweets is not allowed in the classroom.

- We usually use the gerund after a preposition, for example: *interested in, angry about, excited about, dream of*:

Have you thought **of moving** to another country?

Verbs with infinitives

Some verbs are followed by the infinitive. Common verbs that take the infinitive are:

afford, agree, choose, decide, expect, help, hope, learn, manage, need, offer, plan, promise, seem, want, wish, would like/love

My father **learned to drive** when he was seventeen.

- The infinitive is often used with the verb *to be* and adjective (*be* + adjective + infinitive):

It **was easy to solve** this puzzle.

Other expressions often used in this way are: *it's difficult, it's expensive, it's cheap, it's good, it's better*.

- The infinitive is also used to give a reason for doing something (infinitive of purpose):

I'm calling **to invite** you to my party.

want, would like, expect + infinitive

- We can use *want, would like, expect* + infinitive to say what we want to do ourselves:

I **would like to finish** my studies next year.
She **wants to start** a family soon.
He **expects to get** more presents than his brother.

- We can use *want, would like, expect* + pronoun + infinitive to say what we want other people to do:

Ian **would like me to help** him with his homework.
She **wants Peter to apologise** to everybody.
Our teacher **expects us to come** to school on time.

93

Vocabulary

Buskers

1 Divide the following reactions into positive (+), negative (–) or neutral (Ø).

1 object to something —
2 not take any notice
3 appreciate something
4 shout at someone
5 find something entertaining
6 say something is rubbish

2 Complete the text with the words from the box.

> appreciate   found   generous   notice ✓
> object   reacted   rubbish   shouted

My cousin and I do breakdance. Last summer we decided to earn some money by dancing in the street. These are the reactions we got …

Some people didn't take any ¹ _notice_ of us … That was okay – perhaps they were in a hurry or not interested in breakdance. Others ² _____ positively: you could see they ³ _____ our performance entertaining. That was really nice. It's pleasant when people ⁴ _____ your skill.

Some people were really ⁵ _____ ; they gave us more money than we expected. But a few people seemed angry and ⁶ _____ at us. I'm not sure why they reacted so negatively. Perhaps they thought our dancing was ⁷ _____ ; or perhaps they ⁸ _____ to street performers asking for money?

Sophie and Daniel Prior decided to show their breakdance skills out on the street.

Grammar

Modals of deduction

3 ✳ Match sentences 1–4 with a–d to make pairs which have the same meaning.

1 He must be a professional musician.
2 He might be a professional musician.
3 He might not be a professional musician.
4 He can't be a professional musician.

a I'm sure he isn't a professional musician.
b Perhaps he isn't a professional musician.
c I'm sure he is a professional musician.
d Perhaps he is a professional musician.

4 ✳ Complete the answers with *must* or *can't* and the correct verb.

1 Are they brothers?
   They _must be_ brothers. They look very similar.

2 Does she have children?
   She _____ children. She's got too much free time.

3 Is he French?
   He _____ French. He hasn't got a French accent.

4 Do I know her?
   You _____ her. She's famous.

5 Do they live here?
   They _____ here. I've never seen them before.

6 Do they have a lot of money?
   They _____ a lot of money. Just look at this Porsche.

5 ✳✳ Read the description of the situation. Complete the sentences with *may/might (not)* or *could* and the verbs below.

> *We're waiting for Laura to get here from Glasgow. She said her train would arrive in London at 6 p.m. and she'd get a bus to our house. It's 10 p.m. now, she's not here and she isn't answering her mobile.*

> be   be   be ✓   come   have   have

1 Laura's train _may be_ delayed.
2 She _____ her phone with her.
3 Her phone _____ broken.
4 She _____ the right address.
5 She _____ lost.
6 She _____ on the morning train.

6 (**) Match sentences 1–6 to reasons a–f.

1 He must be tired.
2 He can't be hungry yet.
3 He may not come today.
4 He could be joking.
5 He might know how to repair this.
6 He might not understand what you're saying.

a He's already two hours late.
b He's been studying all day.
c I think he's a foreigner.
d He's good at technical things.
e His story is difficult to believe.
f He's just had a big meal.

7 Complete the dialogue with *must, might, may, could, may not* or *can't* and an appropriate verb. Use each form once.

Lily's parents are talking about her.

Jean: I'm really worried about Lily. She doesn't study at all. She just sits in her room all afternoon and listens to music.

Phil: She ¹ _may be_ in love.

Jean: I don't know. She ² _____ a boyfriend though – she doesn't go out with anyone. I'm worried that she ³ _____ learning difficulties.

Phil: Come on! It can't be that. She's very intelligent. Do you think she ⁴ _____ a health problem?

Jean: No, she's been to the doctor's and she's fine.

Phil: I'll tell you what I think. She ⁵ _____ interested in what they're doing at school, that's all. It may be as simple as that.

Jean: Perhaps you're right. After all, it ⁶ _____ really tiring learning all those subjects.

Grammar reference

Modals of deduction (*must, might, may, could, can't*)

To make guesses or deductions about the present and the future, we use *must, might, may, could, can't* + infinitive without *to*.

- We use *must* when you are almost sure/certain that something is true:

*She **must be** terribly unhappy.* (I'm sure she's unhappy)
*You're so sociable – you **must have** many friends.* (I'm certain that you have many friends)

- We use *might, may* or *could* when you think that things/events are possible, but you're not sure:

*Ron **might need** your help with Maths.* (I'm not sure, it's possible that he needs your help)
*She **may be** at home now.* (It's possible that she is at home now)
*A bar of chocolate **could make** her happier.* (It's possible that a bar of chocolate will make her happier)

- We use *might not* and *may not* when you think that things/events are not true or perhaps will not happen:

*They **may not be** on holiday yet.* (Perhaps they're not on holiday yet)
*She **might not come** home before midnight.* (Perhaps she will not come home before midnight)

- We use *can't* when you are almost sure/certain that things/events are not true:

*You **can't work** twelve hours a day.* (It's impossible that you work twelve hours a day)
*She **can't be** in America – I saw her yesterday at school.* (I'm sure she's not in America)

Different modal verbs express different degrees of certainty:

*She **must be** in her thirties.* → <u>I'm sure</u> she's in her thirties.
*She **could/might/may be** in her thirties.* → <u>Perhaps</u> she's in her thirties.
*She **may/might not be** in her thirties.* → <u>Perhaps</u> she's <u>not</u> in her thirties.
*She **can't be** in her thirties.* → <u>I'm sure</u> she's <u>not</u> in her thirties.

Vocabulary

What is art?

1 Look at the photograph and complete the critics' opinions with the words from the box.

> think   reminds   mean   on the right ✓
> in front of   might   of art   beautiful
> style   don't understand

Critic 1: This is a famous photo for peace. There is a woman ¹ _on the right_ . She's holding a flower. The woman is young, I think she ² _____ be a student. She is standing ³ _____ a line of soldiers. This is a great photo, I really like the ⁴ _____ . The photo ⁵ _____ me of a film I watched.

Critic 2: I don't think it's a work ⁶ _____ . It doesn't ⁷ _____ anything to me! I ⁸ _____ what the photographer is trying to say.

Critic 1: Of course it's art! It makes you ⁹ _____ and that's the purpose of art. I think it's very ¹⁰ _____ .

2 Complete the sentences with one letter in each gap.

REAL LIFE **NEWS**   ✕

Home **UK** World Business Technology Science Sport Entertainment

What is art anyway?

¹ _Controversial_ British artist Gavin Turk is back in the news again. His latest piece of artwork, called 'Brillo 5' is a cardboard box made of painted metal. Christies, one of the most famous art auction houses in the world, plans to sell the work at a ² s_ _ _ next month. Experts say it is ³ w_ _ _ _ as much as $30,000. Some ⁴ cr_ _ _ _ _ think his work is rubbish, but others love his work and say he's a ⁵ g_ _ _ _ _ .

Reading

3 Look at the book cover, read the introduction to the story and the key words in the box below. What do you think happens in the story?

> gallery   alarm
> break-in   steals
> police officers
> paintings

The extract is from *44 Scotland Street* by the Scottish writer Alexander McCall Smith. It is about a group of people who live in Scotland Street in Edinburgh. Pat works in an art gallery. Her boss, Matthew, owns the gallery.

4 Read the extract and complete the sentences with the correct names from the box.

> Jimmy Clarke   Pat   the older policeman
> the younger policeman   Matthew

1 _____ arrives at the gallery and discovers the break-in.
2 _____ phones the police.
3 Pat wonders if _____ is responsible for the break-in.
4 _____ is an art thief.
5 _____ says that the alarm probably didn't work properly.
6 _____ thinks he knows who stole the painting.

5 Read the extract again and tick (✓) true or cross (✗) false.

1 ☐ When Pat goes into the gallery the alarm doesn't go off as usual.
2 ☐ Pat felt uneasy because she couldn't see anyone outside the gallery.
3 ☐ The intruder didn't have to break the window to get into the gallery.
4 ☐ Matthew's gallery is doing well at the moment and selling a lot of paintings.
5 ☐ Pat is sure that Matthew broke in to the gallery.
6 ☐ The older policeman is very unhappy that they can't prove who the intruder is.

Things happen at the gallery

Pat arrived slightly early at the gallery the next morning. She was about to go through to the back, when she stopped. Usually, when she came in in the morning, she would hear the alarm and have to type in the number to stop it. This had not happened this morning.

Had the alarm been set? She looked at the control box. Two small red lights went on and off. That was different. Normally it was a single red. Pat looked around. The gallery had a large glass window at the front, and this looked out onto the street. There were people on the pavement, traffic on the road. The door was only a few metres away. But even so, she suddenly felt nervous and now she saw that the door of the room at the back of the gallery was open. She closed that door – always – before she left.

Now she felt frightened, and she ran across the room to switch on the lights. Then, with the gallery lit up, she found the courage to walk over to the inner office door and push it open.

The intruder* had managed to lift the lower part of the window. The glass was not broken, but the lock had been forced and there were small pieces of wood on the floor. Pat picked up the telephone and dialled the emergency code. A comforting voice told her the police would arrive within minutes and not to touch anything. So she stood there wondering what had happened. Why had the alarm not gone off? Why was the office door open? It suggested the intruder had managed to get in through the small window and then been disturbed*.

It suddenly occurred to Pat that a break-in could be quite convenient* for Matthew. He was having difficulty selling any of his paintings; perhaps it would be easier to arrange an insurance claim*.

A few minutes later a police car arrived outside the gallery and two officers got out. Pat opened the front door.

She showed the men the alarm.

'It can't have worked properly,' said the younger policeman.

She led them through to the back room and pointed at the wood on the floor. The older policeman looked at the glass and shook his head.

'No prints* there,' he said. And there's not much we can do, although I can probably tell you who did this.'

Pat listened in surprise. 'But how do you know?'

'After all my time as a policeman, I'm sure about one thing. The same people do the same things all the time. We know who they are and where they live. This was probably done by a man called Jimmy Clarke. He's the person who steals paintings in this city. But of course we can't prove it.'

'It must be difficult for you,' Pat said.

The older policeman smiled. 'Not really, you get used to it.'

* intruder – someone who breaks into a building
* disturb – interrupt, stop someone from doing something
* convenient – something that is convenient gives someone an opportunity, often in a way that is a little dishonest
* insurance claim – insurance is the money you pay a company regularly so they will give you money if something you own is stolen or damaged. A claim is when you ask the insurance company for money
* prints = fingerprints – the marks you leave when your fingers touch an object

Listening

6 You are going to listen to two people discussing the extract *Things happen at the gallery*. Before you listen, choose the most likely explanation for the break-in.

1 ☐ Nobody ever finds out who broke into the gallery or why. It remains a mystery, but each character has his/her own theory about it.

2 ☐ The art thief Jimmy Clarke broke into the gallery. He was planning to steal the best paintings, but then he heard someone outside. He escaped before he could steal any paintings.

3 ☐ Ronnie and Pete, two men who know Matthew, think that there is a painting in the gallery that is worth a lot of money. They decide to break in, but they are disturbed before they can steal the painting.

4 ☐ Matthew's gallery is doing badly and he needs to make some money. He arranges for someone to break in and steal some paintings. Then he plans to claim the money from his insurance.

7 (21) Listen to the conversation and write the numbers of the theories above in the order they are discussed. Which is the correct one?

Order of discussion: ___ , ___ , ___ , ___

The most probable theory is: ___

8 (21) Listen again and underline the correct answers to complete the sentences.

1 Jane *wants/doesn't want* to tell Kevin immediately who broke in to the gallery.

2 Kevin doesn't think it was *an art-thief/Matthew* because that's too obvious.

3 *Kevin/Jane* says that Matthew can't be the thief because he's too honest.

4 Kevin thinks the thieves wanted to steal *a painting/a sculpture* by Peploe.

5 The painting by Peploe could be worth *£400,000/£40,000*.

6 The author *reveals/doesn't reveal* who tried to rob the art gallery at the end of the book.

Writing

A review of an event

1 In **paragraph 1**, give basic information about the band or event. For example, for a festival, give the name of the festival, say who organised it, how often it happens, etc.

2 In **paragraph 2**, say where and when the concert/event was and how many people were there. If you like, give some general information: *the atmosphere was great, the sound quality wasn't very good,* etc.

3 In **paragraph 3**, describe the music/event and how the audience reacted: *they opened/started/began/kicked off with … the audience went wild when they played … the third piece was excellent …*

4 In **paragraph 4**, give a short summary of the event: *To sum up/ In conclusion/ To conclude …* Give your personal opinion: *a wonderful/brilliant/fantastic/awful gig/concert … the best/worst festival I've ever been to …*

5 Give a recommendation: *I would/wouldn't recommend going to see them … it's worth/not worth going to …,* etc.

If you were at the Luto concert last Saturday night, then you'll know how good they were – see our review below.

A concert review

Luto are an American indie rock group from California. The band has four members, lead singer Andrew Weston, guitarist Tim Ellis, keyboard player Tim Childs and drummer Matt Stevens. Weston writes the catchy tunes and entertaining lyrics – he's the real star of the band.

The band played at the Darena last night, one of the city's best small venues, to an audience of over 400. The concert was sold out and the atmosphere in the crowded venue was fantastic. The sound quality was excellent and the video show was great.

They started off with *You're Awful* and the audience really loved it. Although this is the first time they've played in the UK, they were all confident and played well. The highlight of the performance was their single *Love Me* – a hilarious song that combines great music with very funny lyrics. The song made everyone laugh! By the end of the performance, everyone in the audience was singing and dancing.

In conclusion, this was a fantastic gig by a really exciting new band. I recommend Luto for anyone who likes catchy songs with fun, interesting lyrics. They're well-worth seeing live – if you didn't see them this time, then you can see them next month in Leeds. Tell all your friends!

1 Read the concert review quickly. Underline the correct answers.

1 Luto are from the *UK/US*.
2 The concert *was/wasn't* very good.
3 The *best/worst* song they sang was called *Love me*.
4 The writer *recommends/doesn't recommend* people to go and see the band.

2 Read the review again. Find the underlined expressions in the text, then choose the best definitions.

1 Weston writes the catchy tunes
   a music that attracts your attention and is easy to remember
   b music that is very boring and that you forget quickly
2 The concert was sold out
   a There were no more tickets for the concert.
   b There were plenty of tickets for sale.
3 The sound quality was excellent
   a you could hear the music well
   b the songs were very good
4 a hilarious song
   a very sad   b very funny
5 They're well-worth seeing
   a the writer strongly recommends seeing them
   b the writer thinks it was a bad idea to see them

3 Rewrite the sentences using the words from the box.

[sound quality   crowded ✓
catchy   awful   highlight
well-worth seeing]

1 There were a lot of people in the venue.
   The venue was crowded.
2 You could hear the music very well.
   _____
3 They were not good at all.
   _____
4 They were the best band in the festival.
   _____
5 The songs were easy to remember.
   _____
6 It's a good idea to see them live.
   _____

4 Read Olga's notes for her review of a festival. Decide in which paragraph each note should go. Use the notes in boxes 1–5 on page 98 to help you.

- highlight of the evening was the performance by the group Tonic 3 ☐ 3
- exhibitions, great food, live music — at the Exhibition Centre ☐
- great day out for all the family and teens will enjoy the live music in the evening ☐
- festival took place in Manchester — called Manchester Festival ☐
- in the evening three bands: rock band (terrible!) called Metal, a dance band called Tonic (catchy songs, people danced), a jazz band called Rev (good — played 2nd) ☐
- yesterday — about 800 people ☐
- organised by local council ☐
- definitely worth going to — on for three more days (Tonic play again tomorrow night so still possible to see them) ☐

5 Complete the strategies box with the words below.

> logical ✓   final   interesting

A review of an event

- Read the task carefully. Think about what information you can include in each paragraph. Make notes and decide which is the most interesting information.
- Organise your notes into paragraphs. In each paragraph, make sure the sentences are in a ¹ *logical* order.
- Use a variety of adjectives to make your writing more ² _____ .
- Summarise the concert or event in the ³ _____ paragraph. Give your opinion and your recommendation.
- Check the number of words and then check your grammar, punctuation and spelling.

6 Choose one of the tasks and write a review. Use the strategies in exercise 5 to help you. Write 200–250 words.

> Write a review of:
> 1 A festival you have been to.
> 2 The festival Olga went to. (Use the notes in exercise 4.)
> In your review:
> - include information about where and when it was, what kind of entertainment and other things there were (food, music, parades, etc.)
> - include your opinion about what was good/bad about the festival.

Speaking

Asking for and giving advice

7 Choose the best answer.

1 Your friend doesn't look happy. You say:
   a What do you think we should do?
   b What's the matter? ✓

2 You ask your friend why he/she isn't happy. He/She says:
   a What's up?
   b I've got a problem.

3 You want to ask for advice about a problem. You say:
   a Should I try something different?
   b You should try something different.

4 You want to give your friend some advice. You say:
   a I wouldn't do that, if I were you.
   b Should I do that?

5 Your friend has just given you some advice. You say:
   a I think you should listen to me.
   b You're right. That's a good idea.

8 Complete the dialogue with the phrases from the box.

> Can I ask your opinion
> You're right   I think you should
> What's the matter ✓   Sure
> I would get together

Alan: ¹ *What's the matter* , Sarah? You look worried.

Sarah: ² _____ about something, Alan?

Alan: ³ _____ . What's the problem?

Sarah: Well, I used to see a lot of Kate, but she's got a new boyfriend and she never goes out with her friends now.

Alan: ⁴ _____ talk to her. Tell her how you feel.

Sarah: I've already tried that, but she won't listen to me.

Alan: Then ⁵ _____ with Kate's other friends and all talk to her about it.

Sarah: ⁶ _____ , but it's so difficult! Thanks, Alan.

12 what next?

✱	easy to do
✱✱	a bit harder
✱✱✱	extra challenge

Vocabulary

Word families

1 Make nouns from the verbs in the box. Write them in the correct column.

> communicate ✓ develop discover
> educate entertain inform know

Nouns ending in …		
-ation-	ment	other
communication		

2 Form new words from the words in brackets to complete the sentences and fill in the crossword.

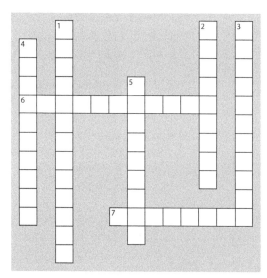

Across

6 Instead of buying your children another (EDUCATION) toy, you might consider spending more time with them.

7 He has a very (CREATE) mind; he produces ten new ideas a day.

Down

1 Millie's not very (COMMUNICATE) today. In fact, she's not speaking to me.

2 More (KNOW) doesn't always make people happier.

3 Thank you for a very (INFORM) meeting; I have learned a lot of useful things.

4 To me, one of the best (INVENT) of the 19th century is the bicycle.

5 The (DISCOVER) of radio waves made it possible to build the telegraph, radio and television.

Grammar

Third conditional

3 ✱ Match the sentence beginnings 1–5 with the endings a–e.

1 If he had come to the party,
2 If the dog hadn't been tied up,
3 If you had left earlier,
4 If I'd known his real character,
5 If she hadn't been so tired,

a you would have caught the train.
b I wouldn't have married him.
c it would have bitten you.
d the accident wouldn't have happened.
e he wouldn't have enjoyed it anyway.

4 ✱✱ Match sentences 1–5 to cartoons a–e. Then choose the correct verb form to complete the sentences.

a ☐
b ☐
c ☑ 1
d ☐
e ☐

1 You *had found/would have found* it if you *had looked/would have* looked carefully.

2 You *had been/would have been* sick if you *had eaten/would have eaten* all those chocolates!

3 I *hadn't spoken/wouldn't have spoken* to him even if he *had spoken/would have spoken* to me.

4 I *hadn't believed/wouldn't have believed* it if I *hadn't seen/wouldn't have seen* it.

5 What *had happened/would have happened* if I *hadn't stopped/wouldn't have stopped*?

5 (✱✱✱) Read Joe's grandma's story and complete the sentences below with the correct form of the verbs in brackets.

> *This happened when I was twenty years old. I was going to fly to Spain for a holiday, but I forgot my passport. I asked the taxi driver to turn back. There was a traffic jam and I missed my flight. The plane crashed and everyone was killed. But I lived on and met my future husband, your granddad, Frank. We got married and had three children, and then they had their own children. And so you were born because forty years ago I left my flat without my passport.*

1 If I _hadn't forgotten_ (not/forget) my passport, I _wouldn't have asked_ (not/ask) the taxi driver to turn back.
2 If there _____ (not/be) a traffic jam, I _____ (not/miss) my plane.
3 If I _____ (not/miss) my plane, I _____ (be) killed.
4 If I _____ (be) killed, I _____ (not/meet) my husband.
5 If we _____ (not/meet), we _____ (not/have) children.

Grammar plus: Modal verbs in conditional sentences

6 (✱✱✱) Complete the second sentence so that it has a similar meaning to the first. Use the word in bold.

1 My boss didn't help me, so we didn't finish the project last week. **could**
If my boss _had helped me, we could have_ _finished the project last week._

2 They didn't invite us, so we didn't come. **might**
If they _____
_____ .

3 He was ill, so he couldn't take part in the competition. **could**
If he _____
_____ .

4 The driver turned immediately, so she didn't hit the cyclist. **might**
If the driver _____
_____ .

5 You weren't there, so we didn't win the match. **could**
If you _____
_____ .

Grammar reference

Third conditional

Form

Condition if + had/hadn't + past participle	Result would/wouldn't + have + past participle
If I **had got up** earlier,	I **wouldn't have missed** the train.
If you **hadn't gone** home so quickly,	she **would have apologised** to you.
If John **had given** you my phone number,	**would** you **have called** me?

- We can begin the sentence with a condition (*if*- clause) or with a result (the main clause):

*If I **hadn't gone** to the party last night, I'**d have done** my History homework.*
*I'**d have done** my History homework **if I hadn't gone** to the party last night.)*

> **Notice!**
> We put a comma (,) only when we start the sentence with the *if*- clause.

*If mum had had more time yesterday**,** she would have taken us to the cinema.*
*Mum would have taken us to the cinema **if** she had had more time yesterday.*

Use of third conditional

- We use the third conditional to talk about imaginary (hypothetical) situations in the past and their imaginary past results:

*If we **had seen** Nick yesterday at school, we **would have told** him about the test.* (= We didn't see Nick yesterday at school, so we didn't tell him about the test.)
*You **wouldn't have been** so brave if I **hadn't gone** with you.* (= You were brave because I went with you.)

Modal verbs in conditional sentences

- In conditional sentences, we can use the modal verb *could* or *might* in the main clause instead of *would*:

*If Peter **had asked** Jill to marry him, she **might have agreed**.* (= perhaps she would have agreed, but she didn't)
*If you **hadn't been** so slow, we **could have caught** the earlier bus.* (= it would have been possible for us to catch the earlier bus, but we didn't)

Vocabulary

Describing objects

1 Put the words from the box into the correct row in the table.

> round ✓ handle leather flat
> metal switch wood pockets
> cylindrical fabric thin

Shapes	*round*
Materials	
Features	

2 Complete questions 1–5 with the words from the box. Then match the questions to answers a–e.

> used shape made features big ✓

1 How _big_ is it?
2 What _____ is it?
3 What's it _____ of?
4 Has it got any special _____ ?
5 What's it _____ for?

a It's got two handles.
b For storing things.
c Some kind of fabric.
d It's flat and wide.
e It's about 50 cm long and 40 cm wide.

3 Match the descriptions 1–4 to the pictures a–d.

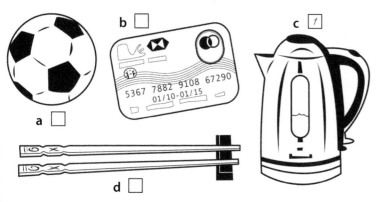

1 It's cylindrical. It's made of metal. It's got a handle and a switch. It's used for boiling water.
2 It's round. It's made of leather. It's used for playing my favourite game.
3 They're long and thin. They're made of wood. They've got decorated handles. They're used for eating.
4 It's flat. It's 8.5 cm long and 5.5 cm wide. It's made of plastic. It's got lots of numbers on it. It's used for paying for things.

Grammar

Quantifiers

4 (✱) Number the quantifiers from the smallest (1) to the largest (5).

I've packed
☐ just a few pairs of socks.
☐ plenty of socks.
[1] no socks.
☐ all my socks.
☐ several pairs of socks.

5 (✱) Underline the correct words to complete the sentences.

1 Don't worry. We've got *plenty of/a little* time. There's no need to hurry at all.
2 *None/Several of* my classmates like football, but Julie and Alex prefer basketball.
3 They bought every carton of juice in the shop. There were *none/a few* left.
4 I just need *a few/a lot of* batteries for the remote control.
5 There were *several/all* people there, but none of them helped us.
6 We've got *plenty of/a bit of* cheese, but not enough for the three of us.

6 (✱✱) Complete the answers with *both, neither, all* or *none*.

1 'Can I borrow your black jacket or your grey one?'
'_Neither_ , I'm afraid. I need them both this week.'
2 'We've got a cheese sandwich and a salmon sandwich. Do you mind which one I take?'
'You can have _____ I'm not hungry at all.'
3 'Which of these papers can I throw out?'
'_____ of them! They're all very important!'
4 'Which of your cousins are coming tomorrow?'
'_____ of them. It's going to be a really big party.'
5 'Did you prefer the first film or the second?'
'I'm afraid I liked _____ of them. I thought they were _____ rather weak.'
6 'Which of the clothes in the fashion show did you finally buy?'
'_____ of them. They were _____ too expensive.'

7 (✱✱) **Complete each sentence with the two words in brackets.**

1 The tourists bought _all_ the mineral water and _every_ sandwich in the shop. (all, every)

2 I like my new room. There's _____ of space and there are _____ large drawers in which I can store things. (several, plenty)

3 I don't need much to be happy: _____ money and _____ friends are enough for me. (a few, a little)

4 'Have you got everything you need for the exam?'
'I've got two calculators and a lot of pens, but _____ of the calculators work and _____ of the pens write.' (none, neither)

5 _____ my parents and _____ my other relatives want me to go to university, but I'd like to become a gardener. (all, both)

8 (✱✱✱) **Complete the gaps in the text with** *both,* ***neither, all*** **or** ***none.***

Blog Site

My whole family is incredibly creative. First of all, _____ my parents are scientists; they work for NASA. ² _____ of my two brothers wanted to be a rocket scientist, but they are ³ _____ computer programmers and they design new software. I'm a bit different from ⁴ _____ four of them: I'm a musician; I compose film music. But there's one thing the whole family has in common. We ⁵ _____ love creating something new, and ⁶ _____ of us would ever want to work from nine to five in an office. Oh, and I want to tell you one more thing: ⁷ _____ of my parents has ever done any work for the military. ⁸ _____ of us have and I hope we never will.

Grammar reference

Quantifiers

We use *all, every, a lot of, plenty of, several, a little bit of, a few* and *no* to talk about quantities.

- We use *all* with countable plural nouns and uncountable nouns, but *every* only with countable singular nouns:

*We ate **all** the apples.*
*She drank **all** the milk.*
*I looked at **every** house.*

- We use *a lot of* and *plenty of* with countable plural nouns and uncountable nouns:

*You've got **a lot of** friends.*
*He has **a lot of** money.*
*Can you bring **plenty of** pencils?*
*There's **plenty of** time.*

- We use *several* with countable plural nouns:

*She's friendly with **several** boys.*

- We use *a little bit of* with uncountable nouns and *a few* with countable plural nouns:

*Just drink **a little bit of** water.*
*The school has **a few** computers.*

- We use *no* with both countable (singular and plural) and uncountable nouns:

*We've got tea but **no** coffee.*
***No** T-shirts allowed.*

both and neither

- We use *both (of)* (= one and the other) and *neither (of)* (= not one or not the other) to talk about two people or things:

***Both** brothers are very intelligent.* (two brothers)
***Both of** them were very expensive.* (two things)
***Neither of** my parents smoke.* (two parents)
***Neither of** the films had a happy end.* (two films)

all and none

- We use *all (of)* and *none of* with plural nouns when we talk about more than two people or things:

***All** my friends came to the party.* (more than two people)
*I wrote five sentences but **all of** them were wrong.* (five sentences – more than two)
***None of** the girls wanted to help me.* (more than two girls)
***None of** the books are worth recommending.* (more than two books)

Vocabulary

Human robots?

1 Complete the first part of the text with the words from the box.

> respond   serve   compassion ✓
> facial expressions   pity

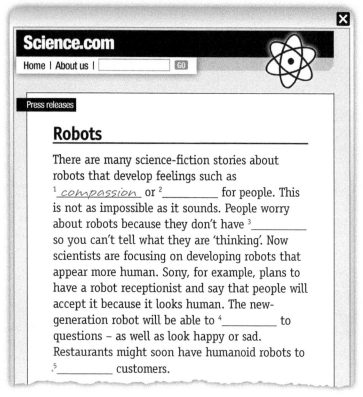

Science.com

Home | About us | [＿＿＿＿＿] **GO**

Press releases

Robots

There are many science-fiction stories about robots that develop feelings such as [1] _compassion_ or [2] _____ for people. This is not as impossible as it sounds. People worry about robots because they don't have [3] _____ so you can't tell what they are 'thinking'. Now scientists are focusing on developing robots that appear more human. Sony, for example, plans to have a robot receptionist and say that people will accept it because it looks human. The new-generation robot will be able to [4] _____ to questions – as well as look happy or sad. Restaurants might soon have humanoid robots to [5] _____ customers.

2 Read the second part of the text and choose the correct answer a, b or c for each gap.

Most people agree that in the future robots will do much more than they do now. They won't just [1] _a_ the housework or [2] ___ of bombs or [3] ___ cars and other machines. They won't just [4] ___ space or under the sea. Robots will be part of our everyday lives. Of course, robots do have some advantages over humans – they don't [5] ___ hungry or tired, they don't worry [6] ___ problems. It's unlikely they will deprive people of jobs and create unemployment. Perhaps our biggest worry should be that they really will [7] ___ the world one day!

1 a	do ✓	**b**	make	**c**	clean
2 a	place	**b**	dispose	**c**	direct
3 a	arrange	**b**	alter	**c**	assemble
4 a	look	**b**	find	**c**	explore
5 a	go	**b**	get	**c**	need
6 a	after	**b**	about	**c**	with
7 a	take in	**b**	take over	**c**	take off

Reading

3 Read the text and choose the best summary.

1 The text is about gadgets that are already available in most countries.

2 The text is about gadgets that you can buy now or that will be available soon.

3 The text is about gadgets that are just science fiction at the moment, although they may be possible some day.

4 Read the text and choose the correct answers.

1 The machine to clean people and clothes
  a is already being used in Japan.
  b is much cheaper now than it used to be.
  c is used in homes and hospitals now.
  d has replaced showers in most Japanese homes.

2 Nuvo
  a uses typical materials such as metal.
  b is the same size as the average humans.
  c can give voice commands.
  d moves like a human.

3 Experts believe that
  a robots will become much more expensive over the next year.
  b many more people will buy personal robots in the near future.
  c companies will not sell many robots over the next few years.
  d sales of robots will grow very slowly in the near future.

4 At the moment, the computer chips in clothes
  a are only for professional athletes.
  b can only measure your body temperature.
  c can show if the body is doing too much.
  d don't yet exist, but scientists are working on the idea.

5 Dyson's fan is
  a more energy-efficient than air conditioning.
  b not very environmentally friendly.
  c shouldn't be used if you have young children.
  d has a different type of blade to traditional fans.

5 Answer the questions.

1 In Japan, who is the machine used to wash?

＿＿＿＿＿＿＿＿＿＿＿＿＿＿＿＿＿＿＿＿

2 How much will Nuvo cost?

＿＿＿＿＿＿＿＿＿＿＿＿＿＿＿＿＿＿＿＿

3 What two types of health problems could the new chips be used for?

＿＿＿＿＿＿＿＿＿＿＿＿＿＿＿＿＿＿＿＿

4 Where would the chip send a message?

＿＿＿＿＿＿＿＿＿＿＿＿＿＿＿＿＿＿＿＿

5 How does the price of Dyson's fan compare with a normal fan?

＿＿＿＿＿＿＿＿＿＿＿＿＿＿＿＿＿＿＿＿

New technology

Some of these ideas may sound like science fiction – in fact, they already exist and could be part of our everyday lives soon.

Human 'washing machine'

Why have a shower and wash your clothes separately? Wouldn't you prefer to step into a gadget that could instantly clean you and your clothes? In Japan, they've already got a special machine that does exactly that. At present, it's used in hospitals for patients who can't easily move. It's expensive – it costs $50,000 – but the price will drop as scientists develop better models. In the future every home could have one, and the ordinary shower might become a thing of the past.

Personal robots

Robot technology is getting better all the time. Two companies plan to start selling a new personal robot later this year. The robot, called Nuvo, doesn't have any wires or handles and it's not made of metal – it's a humanoid robot that uses totally new materials. It's 35 cm tall and can walk like humans, understand voice commands and send video from its 'eyes' to a videophone. It costs $4,600, so it's not cheap, but experts think sales – at present around $4 billion – will grow to $14 billion by next year.

Clothes for health

The idea of combining clothes with computer chips isn't new. Computer chips in clothes can already measure body temperature and heart rate to detect if your body is working too hard – some professional athletes use these smart clothes during training. Now scientists are working on chips that can analyse the chemicals in your sweat. The device could detect high stress levels or if people with diabetes* have too much sugar in their blood. In the future, the chips could send the user a text message to tell them they need to relax, eat some food or go to a doctor.

Keeping cool

British inventor James Dyson has developed an amazing new table fan for cooling air. It doesn't have blades, so there is no risk of children hurting themselves. It uses 98% less energy than air conditioning, so it's good for the environment. too. The big disadvantage is that it costs around $300, so it's about ten times more expensive than a traditional fan.

Traditional fan

blade

Dyson's new bladeless fan

* diabetes – a medical condition, caused when the body does not produce enough insulin (a substance that reduces the amount of sugar in the blood)

Reading

Multiple choice

1 Read the first paragraph of an article about robots in film and the multiple-choice question. Mark each option correct (✓) or wrong (✗), and complete the explanation. There is only one correct option.

Robots in film

Did you know that the word 'robot' was used in science fiction before it was used in science? The Czech writer Karel Capek created it for his 1920 play *R.U.R*, which stands for Rossum's Universal Robots. In the play, Rossum's factory produces human-like robots to serve people, but they turn into evil killing machines and take over the world.

In the play *R.U.R.*,

a ☒ Karel Čapek used a new word created by scientists.

The word was created by *Karel Čapek*.

b ☐ A factory makes robots designed to kill people.

The robots are designed to _____.

c ☐ Robots get out of control.

The robots _____.

d ☐ The company R.U.R. takes over the world.

The _____ take over the world.

  Exam TIP

The correct option expresses the same meaning as the text in other words. The wrong options may contain words which also appear in the text, but the meaning of the whole sentence is different.

2 Read the rest of the article. Choose the correct answers.

1 *Metropolis* was the first film in which
   a there was a funny-looking robot.
   b a mad scientist built a robot.
   c a robot looked like a real woman.
   d people fought robots.

2 It is difficult to fight robots with human-like bodies because
   a they look threatening.
   b you need a 'Voigt-Kampff machine'.
   c they kill people.
   d you may not know they aren't real people.

3 The robots C3PO, R2D2, David and WALL-E are similar because
   a they aren't evil.
   b they are funny.
   c they want to be loved by humans.
   d they are hard-working.

4 David in *Artificial Intelligence: A.I.*
   a asks a lot of questions.
   b has a human-like need for love.
   c feels sympathy towards people.
   d wants to have rights.

Since then, humans have fought evil robots in hundreds of books and films. Some of the early film robots would look rat[her] funny to us today: big metal boxes with car headlights for ey[es] But the 'machine human' in Fritz Lang's 1927 silent classic *Metropolis* had an attractive, modern design. In the film, a m[ad] scientist created a mechanical copy of the good heroine M[aria] to deceive people. The 'fake Maria' was the first female rob[ot in] a movie, and the first one made to look like a real person.

Some film robots are designed to look mechanical and threaten[ing] Gort in *The Day the Earth Stood Still* – both in the original 1[951] movie and in its 2008 remake – is huge and metallic. He h[as a] smooth face with no features, only a slit where the eyes sho[uld] be. Through this slit he projects a laser beam which can des[troy] tanks and aeroplanes. Other movie robots look exactly like humans, which makes it difficult to recognise and fight them. In *Blade Runner* (1982), a special test using a 'Voigt-Kampf[f] machine' is necessary to tell 'replicants' – humanoid robots

Listening

Sentence completion

3 You are going to listen to a radio programme about the artist, Blu. Before you listen, read sentences 1–3. What kind of information is needed in each gap? Choose the correct options a–c for the sentences 1–3.

1 ☐ 'The Influencers' is the name of a festival of _____ .

2 ☐ Blu has been working on his graffiti for _____ days.

3 ☐ The painting shows _____ .

a an object, person or animal
b a type of art
c a number

Exam TIP

Before you listen, read the sentences you will have to complete and think about the kind of information that is needed in each gap.

4 ㉒ Listen twice to the first part of the programme and complete the sentences in exercise 3 with one or two words or a number.

5 ㉓ Listen twice to the rest of the programme and complete sentences 1–7 with one or two words or a number.

1 Some people are pleased that the wall is _____ .

2 Some people think the picture is an _____ .

3 Wall animation is made by painting pictures on a wall and _____ them.

4 At the beginning the film *Muto* shows a creature with _____ .

5 The creature changes _____ many times.

6 *Muto* is almost _____ long.

7 A video of the wall painting should be available on _____ soon.

---

n people. And the terrifying killing machine Terminator looks
actly like … Arnold Schwarzenegger.

t all film robots are evil. Most of us remember C3PO and R2D2,
funny and loveable pair of friends from *Star Wars*. In Steven
elberg's *Artificial Intelligence: A.I.*, David, the little android*
who wants to be loved, has all our sympathy. Children and
lts alike loved WALL-E, the hardworking little robot who falls
ove with the elegant EVE in the Oscar-winning animated film.

ficial Intelligence* was the first film in which an android was the
n character. In *WALL-E*, all the important characters are robots.
se stories raise new questions: Can robots have feelings?
can they ever have 'human' rights? Some day we may
e to answer these questions in the world outside the cinema.

roid – a robot that looks completely human

Use of English

Sentence transformation

6 Complete the second sentence so that it means the same as the first. Use no more than three words.

1 He wasn't killed because the firemen arrived immediately.
If the firemen _hadn't arrived_ immediately, he would have been killed.

2 They are cleaning the plane now.
The plane _____ now.

3 I must ask the optician to test my eyes next week.
I must have _____ next week.

4 I'm sure she's a well-known artist.
She _____ a well-known artist.

5 Ben asked Ellen, 'What kind of art do you like best?'
Ben asked Ellen what kind of art _____ best.

7 Match the sentences in exercise 6 to the structures you used to complete them.

a ☐ have something done
b ☐ modals of deduction
c ☐ reported question
d ☐ the passive
e ☐ the third conditional

Exam TIP

Certain typical structures often appear in sentence transformation tasks. It is a good idea to learn them.

8 Complete the second sentence so that it means the same as the first. Use no more than three words.

1 Jessica asked Oliver, 'Where do you show your paintings?'
Jessica asked Oliver where _____ paintings.

2 Perhaps robots have human emotions.
Robots _____ human emotions.

3 He is finishing the painting right now.
The painting _____ right now.

4 Grace asked someone to cut her hair last week.
Grace had _____ last week.

5 The concert wasn't a success because we didn't prepare it properly.
If we'd prepared the concert properly, it _____ a success.

Vocabulary & Grammar

1 Choose the best word a, b or c to complete the sentences.

1 I found the concert very _b_ .
   a controversial   b entertaining ✓
   c kind

2 Her new handbag is made of ___ .
   a handle   b leather   c flat

3 We went to a heavy metal ___ .
   It was brilliant!
   a play   b show   c gig

4 Robots are already used for the ___ of bombs.
   a exploration   b assembly
   c disposal

5 Under the new ___ the orchestra improved.
   a conductor   b musician   c critic

6 What do you call a ___ object used for playing football?
   a round   b fabric   c rectangular

7 Twenty children will give ___ of ballet.
   a a festival   b a performance
   c show

/6

2 Complete the sentences with one letter in each gap.

1 He is a great artist and his paintings are **w** _orth_ millions.

2 I've listened to many of his records but I'd like to see him on **s** _ _ _ _ .

3 The lamp is made of metal and has got a **s** _ _ _ _ _ which turns it on and off.

4 I **o** _ _ _ _ _ to children begging for money in the street. They should be at school.

5 I loved the play and I could see that other people in the **a** _ _ _ _ _ _ _ liked it too.

6 I wish you could help me with the **h** _ _ _ _ _ _ _ _ . I hate ironing and washing-up.

/5

3 Complete the conditional sentences with the correct form of the verbs in brackets.

1 I'd have finished my studies if I _hadn't become_ (not/become) seriously ill.

2 If you _____ (not/shout) at me, I'd have gone shopping with you.

3 They _____ (win) if they'd played a bit better.

4 Would she have come if I _____ (invite) her?

5 We _____ (not/be) late for the meeting yesterday if we _____ (not/miss) the bus.

/5

4 <u>Underline</u> the correct words to complete the sentences.

1 I hope *getting/to get* a good job in the future.

2 I've got one brother and one sister. *Neither/None* of them like sport.

3 My husband can't stand *getting up/to get up* early in the morning.

4 The professor wants to talk to *every/all* student individually.

5 *Reading/To read* is not my favourite activity.

6 After finishing school, I plan *studying/to study* Medicine.

7 I've got *a little/a few* money to spare.

8 It's good *revising/to revise* the material the day before the test.

9 It's really dark – it *might/must* be very late.

10 No, it *couldn't/can't* be John. He's on his way to New York now.

11 I'm not sure what it is – it *can/might* be some kind of a gadget.

/10

5 Complete the gaps with the correct form of the words in brackets.

Schools of the future
Many people think that schools in the future will be totally ¹ _different_ (differ) from today. The ² _____ (invent) of the computer has already changed the way children are taught at school, and new technological ³ _____ (develop) will certainly bring more changes. A big question is: in twenty years' time, will we still need teachers to ⁴ _____ (education) our children or will they get all their ⁵ _____ (know) from the internet? This is not easy to answer – only time will tell.

/4

Reading

6 a Read the text. Complete the gap in each statement 1–5 with no more than three words using the information in the text.

Scientists have designed a new machine – a robot which recognises and responds to human emotions. The robot looks exactly like the famous scientist, Albert Einstein. It is made of special material that allows it to change facial expressions. The mesh-like material that makes up the robot's face is so detailed it looks like real human skin.

The robot's designers chose Einstein, the Nobel Prize-winning physicist famous for his theory of relativity, because he was one of the most brilliant scientists of all time. They also chose Einstein because his face is very well known and he appears 'loveable.'

David Hanson, who designed the robot, explained that it was important to develop machines that know what human beings are feeling. If, in the future, robots become as intelligent as human beings, he wants them 'to use their intellectual powers for the good of civilisation. In a way, we're planting the seeds for the survival of humanity.'

The robot uses computer software that helps it to understand hundreds of human expressions, such as sadness, anger, fear, happiness and confusion. It can also recognise a person's age, and whether they are male or female.

Javier Movellan, who designed the software, said: 'Developing a robot like this one teaches us how sensitive we are to biological movement and facial expressions, and when we get it right, it's really astonishing.' He added that in the future the robot could be used in museums to help people from different cultures to understand one another. It could also be used to help to teach children with learning difficulties, such as autism*, how to recognise different facial expressions and what they mean.

*autism – brain disorder that begins in early childhood and can cause problems with communication, relationships with other people and everyday behaviour.

1 The robot is modelled on _Albert Einstein_ .

2 One of the reasons to choose the scientist was _____ , which is easily recognisable.

3 According to David Hanson, in the future robots might match human _____ .

4 Apart from people's emotions, the robot also distinguishes their _____ .

5 The robot might have _____ applications in the future.

b Choose the correct answer.

6 The best title of this article is ___ .

  a Robot copy of Albert Einstein.
  b Machines help our civilisation.
  c As intelligent as Albert Einstein.
  d New robots have emotions.

/5

Communication

7 Complete the description of a picture with one word in each gap.

The picture [1] _shows_ several people on the beach In the [2] _____ there's something that looks like a ship, but it's too far away to see clearly. [3] _____ the centre of the picture, two people are looking at the sunset. It [4] _____ be a late summer evening. The people [5] _____ very happy and relaxed. On the left I can [6] _____ a little boy playing in the water with a big dog. [7] _____ are no more people in water. The picture [8] _____ me of my last summer holiday in Spain.

/7

8 Complete the gaps to complete the conversation.

1 Tom: Guess what object I have in mind.
  Ian: Okay. What [1] _is it made of_ ?
  Tom: Leather, sometimes plastic or metal.
  Ian: What [2] _____ ?
  Tom: Rectangular.
  Ian: What features [3] _____ ?
  Tom: It's got holes in it and a buckle.
  Ian: How [4] _____ ?
  Tom: It depends on the trousers!
  Ian: What [5] _____ ?
  Tom: For holding up your trousers.
  Ian: Is it a belt?
  Tom: Yes.

2 Ann: What's [6] _____ , Kate? You look sad.
  Kate: It's my boyfriend again. [7] _____ opinion about something?
  Ann: Sure, what is it?
  Kate: It's that he never calls me. What [8] _____ I should do?
  Ann: Have you talked to him about it?
  Kate: Yes, but it hasn't changed anything. I still have to call him first.
  Ann: I think you [9] _____ something different. Stop calling him and see what happens.
  Kate: Great idea! I'll do it.

/8

Marks

Vocabulary & Grammar	/30 marks
Reading	/5 marks
Communication	/15 marks
Total:	/50 marks

Reading

1 Read the text about governesses.
Tick (✓) true, cross (✗) false or
write (?) if there is no information.

1 ☐ All governesses were
treated badly.

2 ☐ There are many governesses
in books because their
difficult life was interesting
to write about.

3 ☐ In the book *Emma*,
Miss Taylor is happy after
she gets married.

4 ☐ The governess in the book
Agnes Grey is well treated by
the people she works for.

5 ☐ Jane Eyre falls in love with
Mr Rochester.

6 ☐ All the books mentioned in
the article end in a similar
way for the governess
characters.

/6

Listening

2 ㉔ Listen to four people talking
about their work. Match speakers
1–4 to statements a–e. There is one
extra statement.

1 ☐   2 ☐   3 ☐   4 ☐

a In my job I have to be very
well organised.

b My job is respectable and
well paid.

c The thing I enjoy most is
chatting with customers.

d I enjoy some things about
my job, but my employer is
too strict.

e My work is very repetitive
and badly paid.

/4

Governesses in literature

In the nineteenth century, thousands of women in
Britain had to earn their living as governesses, educating
the children of wealthy families. Some were treated badly;
others became almost like family members. One thing was
true about all governesses: they were completely dependent
on their employers. Many would become poor in old age,
as their salaries were too low for them to be able to save
much. The only way to achieve independence and security
was to find a husband, but it was hard for governesses to
meet young men they might marry.

The difficult situation of governesses provided interesting
material for stories: that is why they are present, often as
important characters, in many nineteenth-century novels.

In Jane Austen's *Emma* (1815), for example, the kind
governess Miss Taylor is almost like a mother to Emma for
many years, after her real mother's death. When the girl is
twenty, Miss Taylor marries a wealthy man and
becomes the grown-up Emma's neighbour and friend.

The three Brontë sisters, now famous as writers, all worked
as governesses at some stage in their lives. Anne Brontë
described her experience of teaching in *Agnes Grey*. The
heroine, Agnes, works as a governess to help her family.
Her employers treat her badly, and the children she teaches
are spoilt and selfish. In the end, however, Agnes gets
married and is happy.

Probably the best-known governess in English literature
is Jane Eyre in the 1847 novel by Charlotte Brontë. Jane is
poor and has no parents; but she is also intelligent, artistic
and independent, and has a strong personality. She gets a
job as a governess in the house of the mysterious Mr
Rochester. Mr Rochester soon notices that Jane is much
more interesting than the beautiful, rich lady everyone
expects him to marry. He falls in love with Jane, but his
house holds a dark secret, and many dramatic things
happen before they can finally get married.

It is easy to see that the only happy ending all those
authors could think of for the governesses in their books
was marriage. They were right. At that time there were no
other opportunities for women. The only way to become
financially secure was to get married – in real life this did
not happen quite as often as it did in novels.

Use of English

3 Read about the scientist Maria Skłodowska-Curie. Complete the text with words from the box. There is one extra word.

> as career ✓ conditions degree
> educate for her in sack secondary
> which who

Maria Skłodowska-Curie

You have probably heard of Maria Skłodowska-Curie, the first woman to win a Nobel prize. But did you know about the difficult beginnings of her scientific ¹ _career_ ? Maria's mother died when the girl was eleven, and her father, ² _____ was a teacher, couldn't afford to ³ _____ his daughters. After finishing ⁴ _____ school, Maria and her sister Bronisława agreed to help each other get a university education. In 1887 Bronisława went to Paris to study medicine and Maria got a job ⁵ _____ a governess to help pay for her sister's studies. However, she fell in love with the son of her employers and got the ⁶ _____ . In 1891, after Bronisława finished university and got married, Maria joined her in Paris. In two years she got a ⁷ _____ in Physics and then in Mathematics from the Sorbonne. Soon afterwards she met her future husband Pierre Curie and began further studies, specialising ⁸ _____ radioactivity. Working in very difficult ⁹ _____ , Maria and Pierre discovered the radioactive elements polonium and radium. They received their first Nobel Prize in 1903, while Maria was still in ¹⁰ _____ thirties. Two years later Pierre was killed in an accident. Alone with two small daughters and broken-hearted, Maria continued her scientific work, ¹¹ _____ brought her a second Nobel Prize in 1911.

/10

4 Complete the text with the correct form of the words in brackets.

Decision time

Soon it'll be time to make ¹ _decisions_ (decide) about the future. I'll have to decide how I'm going to earn a ² _____ (live). So how do I choose?

When I was five, I wanted to be a ³ _____ (sail). I loved the sea and it seemed like a perfect place to spend my life. At the age of ten, I decided to be an IT ⁴ _____ (consult), because I liked playing computer games. At fourteen I came up with my most ⁵ _____ (ambition) goal so far: to become a ⁶ _____ (science) and find a ⁷ _____ (solve) to the problem of global warming.

All my friends are going through the same process. There's a lot of talk about how to be ⁸ _____ (success). But some people seem to understand success in one way only: a job with a big company and a high salary. My goal in life is not to be ⁹ _____ (wealth); it is to be happy. I'd like to do things I enjoy and that give me ¹⁰ _____ (satisfy). What's the point of a huge salary if you're ¹¹ _____ (happy) all the time? I may choose sailing as a career after all …

/10

Marks

Reading	/6 marks
Listening	/4 marks
Use of English	/20 marks
Total:	/30 marks

My brother Jimmy

IN STORIES, STEP-FAMILIES ARE USUALLY TERRIBLE.
TONY HAS A DIFFERENT STORY TO TELL.

My dad died soon after I was born. I couldn't really be sad about it because I never knew him. It was always just me and my mum, and in fact I was quite happy. Mum looked after me, played with me and read to me. I was so young I didn't realise how difficult it was for her.

One day when I was six we were in the park together. I was playing alone because there weren't any other kids my age. And then this boy and his dad came along. They had a ball and they started kicking it around; you could see they were having a great time. I stopped playing and just stood there looking at them. The dad noticed me and invited me to join in. I had so much fun, and Mum watched me and smiled. When it was time to go home, she thanked the boy's dad again and again.

We started meeting in the park regularly. Jimmy and I got on very well. We played together and our parents talked. We found out Jimmy's mum had left them years before. One Saturday we all went back to our place; my Mum cooked a fantastic dinner, and we all helped her. Another Saturday Bob and Mum read to us together, doing the voices of the different characters in The 101 Dalmatians.

After about six months Mum asked me if I'd like to live with Jimmy and Bob, as a family. I didn't understand why she looked so nervous. Of course I wanted to live with them! Jimmy was my best mate and his dad was great. I had no reason to be jealous: we were all a lot happier together.

A few months later we celebrated our parents' wedding. We've been living together ever since. It's great to have a mother and a father. We're sixteen now and Jimmy is still my best friend. I never call him a 'step-brother', and when we say we're brothers, people look just a little bit surprised … because there's one thing I haven't told you yet. I'm white and he's black.

Reading

1 **Read the story and complete sentences 1–10 with one or two words according to the information in the text.**

1 After his father's _____ Tony lived with his mother.

2 Tony says he did not feel _____ .

3 Jimmy and his father played _____ in the park.

4 Tony, Jimmy and their parents did various activities together, such as _____ and reading.

5 Bob is the name of _____ .

6 Tony's mum felt _____ when she talked to him about living together with Jimmy and Bob.

7 Tony did not feel _____ because he saw everyone was happier together.

8 Jimmy and Tony have been living together since their parents got _____ .

9 Tony does not like describing Jimmy as his _____ .

10 People find it _____ when Tony and Jimmy say they are brothers.

/5

Listening

2 **(25) Listen to a radio programme about getting to school by bus. Listen to the recording twice and choose the correct answer.**

1 Some students don't take a bus to school because
a the journey is too long.
b buses run at inconvenient times.
c ticket prices are too high.

2 Special bus services are sometimes organised by
a schools and parents.
b parents and bus companies.
c schools and bus companies.

3 The kind of bad behaviour that happens most often on buses is
a vandalism. b smoking. c fighting.

4 The drivers on some school buses
a number the seats.
b are friendly and helpful.
c fasten the young children's seatbelts for them.

5 Students are discouraged from doing any damage because
a the driver is watching them.
b there are cameras on the buses.
c if they do any damage, they have to pay.

6 Parents think that young children
a have few behaviour problems.
b are safe on the special buses.
c are an example to others.

/3

Use of English

3 Choose the best word or phrase a, b or c to complete the gaps in the text.

◄ ► C + 🔒 http://movinghouseblogspot.com · Q▾ Google

moving house blogs 》》》

HOME | BLOGS | CONTACT

⊙ Posted by Jessie on 17 July

New house!!

My family has just moved into a new house. We ¹ _a_ in it for a week now. It still isn't quite finished: for example, the attic room ² ___ right now. And I think we're going to have a dishwasher ³ ___ next week. But it's already great. In our old flat, I ⁴ ___ a room with my sister Claire, and we didn't always get ⁵ ___ that well. Now I've got a big room all to myself and I love it. I've already told everyone they must knock ⁶ ___ the door if they want to come in. Unfortunately, Mum's already started nagging me to tidy up when I ⁷ ___ a mess, which I always do.

We live further from my school than before, but there are good cycle ⁸ ___ all the way, so I'm going to cycle ⁹ ___ it rains. When the weather ¹⁰ ___ really bad in winter, I'll take a bus. If I ¹¹ ___ my own car, I could drive and pick up my friends on the way ... But that's just in my dreams for now.

⊙ Posted by Phil on 17 July

---

1 a have been living ✓ **b** are living **c** lived
2 a is being painted **b** is painting **c** paints
3 a installed **b** install **c** installing
4 a have been sharing **b** shared **c** have shared
5 a around **b** out **c** on
6 a on **b** in **c** to
7 a have **b** do **c** make
8 a roads **b** lanes **c** streets
9 a if **b** when **c** unless
10 a gets **b** will get **c** is going to get
11 a have **b** had **c** will have

/10

4 Complete the text with one word in each gap.

Help save England's butterflies

Twenty years ¹ _ago_ there were thousands of butterflies in the English countryside. If you went for a walk today, you'd ² _____ lucky to see one or two. Butterflies are among our most endangered animals. Here are three ways ³ _____ which you can help protect them. First of ⁴ _____ , butterflies visit gardens to drink nectar from flowers. If you have a garden, plant the kinds ⁵ _____ flowers that butterflies like ⁶ _____ feed on (you can find a list on www.ukbutterflies.co.uk). Secondly, buy fruit and vegetables from producers ⁷ _____ use environmentally friendly farming methods. Intensive farming destroys the type ⁸ _____ environment butterflies need ⁹ _____ live. Thirdly, how ¹⁰ _____ becoming a volunteer? You can take a walk in the countryside and record the types of butterflies ¹¹ _____ see. Or join a working party at ¹² _____ wildlife sanctuary and ¹³ _____ some time cutting weeds and managing butterfly sites.

/12

Marks	
Reading	/5 marks
Listening	/3 marks
Use of English	/22 marks
Total:	/30 marks

Reading

1 **Read the story and choose the correct answer.**

1 The police officer phones Mrs Derwent because her robot
   a has been lost.
   b has been in an accident.
   c has committed a crime.
   d has upset someone.

2 Mrs Derwent presses a button on the robot because she
   a wants it to stop talking.
   b wants the officer to know what she said to it.
   c wants to switch it off.
   d wants it to give her the fruit.

3 Bi1 took the fruit because
   a it was upset and confused.
   b the instructions weren't recorded properly.
   c it misunderstood the instructions.
   d Mrs Derwent told it to do it.

4 The software DECALOG
   a stops robots from breaking the law.
   b helps robots understand instructions.
   c helps robots do their work.
   d may cause a robot to shut down.

5 Billy didn't install DECALOG because
   a he didn't know about it.
   b the central unit shut down.
   c he was ill when he programmed the robot.
   d his teacher hadn't mentioned it.

6 The woman officer thinks that Billy
   a should get a job.
   b has behaved badly.
   c did the right thing.
   d is very talented.

/6

Billy's first robot

Mrs Derwent sat down comfortably on the sofa, put on her old-fashioned headphones, and looked out of the window at Bi1 walking to the shops. It was nice of little Billy to build this clever robot for his grandma.

Half an hour later the phone rang. The screen showed a friendly-looking man in the silver uniform of the city police.

'Mrs Derwent?'

'Yes.'

'Peter Naughton, City Police … May I ask if you've got a domestic robot called Bi1?'

'Yes. Why? Has there been an accident?'

'I'm afraid your robot has just broken into a shop and stolen some fruit. May we come and talk to you?'

Five minutes later two officers entered Mrs Derwent's apartment with Bi1 between them. The robot looked upset and confused.

'I'm a good robot!' it kept repeating. 'I followed instructions!'

'Mrs Derwent, what instructions did you give to Bi1?' asked Officer Naughton.

'Well, I asked it to buy fruit … we can check.' The old lady touched the 'replay last command' button on the robot's back. Speaking in her voice, Bi1 said:

'And get some lovely oranges and pineapples, please, my dear.'

'I see: Bi1 doesn't know that 'get' means 'buy'… But I still don't understand … It shouldn't be possible …' said the other officer, a young woman. 'Where did you buy this robot?'

'My grandson made it at school.'

'Could we talk to your grandson?'

Eight-year-old Billy was summoned from his room. The woman officer smiled.

'Hello, young inventor … You've made an impressive robot, but something's gone wrong with it. It doesn't seem to know that you mustn't take things from shops without paying. Tell me, when you programmed it, you did install DECALOG, didn't you?'

'Install what?'

'Surely your Robotics teacher has told you every domestic robot must have the anti-crime software DECALOG installed?'

'Could that be a lesson you missed?' said Mrs Derwent. 'Remember, you had that cold last month.'

'Right, that would explain it … but … without DECALOG the central unit shouldn't work at all,' said Officer Naughton. 'It should just shut down immediately.'

'Well, it did shut down …' explained little Billy. 'But then I worked on it a bit and got it going.'

The woman officer laughed out loud.

'Right … Mrs Derwent, I'm sure Orsi Electronics would be interested to know your eight-year-old grandson has deactivated their protection software. Maybe they should offer him a job!'

Listening

2 (26) **Listen to four news items. Match items 1–4 to headlines a–e. There is one extra headline.**

1 ☐　　2 ☐　　3 ☐　　4 ☐

a Fifteen crimes in ten minutes

b Thieves not big cat lovers

c Robber gets prison sentence

d Daring escape

e Teenage driver 'wanted to impress girlfriend'

/4

Use of English

3 **Read the text below. In some of the lines there is a word which should not be there. Tick (✓) the correct lines. If a line has a word which should not be there, circle the word.**

Man survives six floor fall

1 A window cleaner who fell from the sixth floor of　✓

2 an office building in Dublin (in) last week has

3 survived with only a minor injuries. Frank Doyle,

4 22, told our reporter how his security equipment

5 has failed. One of his colleagues tried to repair

6 it, while another he tried to pull up Mr Doyle,

7 who was holding on with his bare hands. Eventually

8 they both became too much tired and Mr Doyle

9 fell 20 metres. A second security line was broke.

10 Fortunately an overhanging roof and a third-floor

11 balcony which slowed down his fall. Mr Doyle

12 has broken a leg, but otherwise he is being fine.

/10

4 **Complete the second sentence so that it has a similar meaning to the first sentence. Use no more than three words.**

1 I'm not allowed to play heavy metal music after 11 p.m.

   They don't _let me play_ heavy metal music after 11 p.m.

2 I sprained my ankle, so I didn't go to ski camp.

   If I _____ my ankle, I would have gone to ski camp.

3 I played in a band when I was at school.

   I used _____ in a band when I was at school.

4 Someone has found the stolen painting.

   The stolen painting _____ .

5 I regret not studying for the test last weekend.

   I wish _____ for the test last weekend.

6 I'm going to take my jacket to the cleaner's this week.

   I'm going to _____ cleaned this week.

7 I'm sure he's under a lot of pressure these days.

   He _____ under a lot of pressure these days.

8 Kate asked Daniel, 'Did you like the concert?'

   Kate asked Daniel if _____ the concert.

9 Greg started working for this newspaper ten years ago.

   Greg _____ for this newspaper for ten years.

10 They are printing my story right now.

   My story _____ right now.

11 'Don't touch anything in the room,' the policeman said to us.

   The policeman told us _____ anything in the room.

/10

Marks

Reading　　　　　　/6 marks

Listening　　　　　/4 marks

Use of English　　/20 marks

Total:　　　　　　/30 marks

country and society

crime and law
arrest (v)
authorities (n)
ban (v)
break in (v)
cell (n)
council (n)
court (n)
crime (n)
damage (n)
defence lawyer (n)
deserve (v)
drunk (adj)
fair (adj)
fine (n)
get into trouble (v)
graffiti (n)
law (n)
looter (n)
murder (v)
prison (n)
prison sentence (n)
prosecutor (n)
punishment (n)
release (v)
steal (v)
threaten (v)
witnesses (n)

economy
poverty (n)
billion (n)
developed country (n)
developing world (n)
population (n)
trend (n)

politics
democratic (adj)
campaigner (n)

demonstrate (v)
dictator (n)
government (n)
political (adj)
politician (n)
protestor (n)
vote (v)
(political) views (n)

culture

art
abstract (adj)
canvas (n)
conceptual artist (n)
drawing (n)
exhibition (n)
fashion show (n)
gallery (n)
impression (n)
modern art (n)
painting (n)
phenomenon (n)
portrait (n)
presentation (n)
sculpture (n)
style (n)
swirl (n)

cultural events
(cultural) event (n)
attend (v)
auction (n)
audience (n)
ceremony (n)
concert (n)
contestants (n)
create (v)
dance (n)
era (n)
highlight (n)
hold (organise) (v)

lighting (n)
pastime (n)
performers (n)
prize money (n)
set (v)
set (n)
take part (v)
take place (v)
ticket (n)

describing artists and their work
cool (adj)
appreciate (v)
atmosphere (n)
comment (n)
controversial (adj)
entertaining (adj)
feel sorry (for) (v)
harmful (adj)
masterpiece (n)
mindless (adj)
react (positively) (v)
remind (me of) (v)
take notice (v)
ugly (adj)

literature
crime thriller (n)
extract (n)
main character (n)
mystery (adj)
novel (n)
novel (n)
novelist (n)
published (adj)
writer (n)

music
audience (n)
band (n)
bass guitarist (n)
busker (n)
classical (adj)

concert (n)
conductor (n)
contemporary (adj)
drummer (n)
duet (n)
(rock) festival (n)
gig (n)
guitarist (n)
heavy metal (adj)
heavy metal (n)
hit (n)
instrument (n)
keyboard player (n)
live (concert) (adj)
lyrics (n)
microphone (n)
musical (n)
musician (n)
(backing) musician (n)
opera (n)
orchestra (n)
soul (n)
(great) sound (n)

newspapers and magazines
article (n)
cartoon (n)
celebrity (n)
critic (n)
gossip column (n)
headline (n)
horoscope (n)
human interest (n)
incident (n)
joke (n)
media (n)
news article (n)
pose (for a picture) (v)
(the) press (n)
print (v)
privacy (n)
publicity (n)
review (n)
scandal (n)
sports news (n)
statement (n)

television and film
celebrity (n)
critic (n)
director (n)
famous (adj)
game show (n)
horror (adj)
reality TV (n)
recording (n)
review (n)
series (n)
soap opera (n)
studio (n)
talent show (n)
viewer (n)

theatre
act (v)
costume (n)
decorations (n)
drama (n)
performance (n)
performing arts (n)
play (n)
stage (n)
street performer (n)

family and social life

family
cousin (n)
distant (adj)
elder (brother) (adj)
great (aunt/uncle) (adj)
little (sister) (adj)
only child (n)
relative (n)
sibling (n)
step-brother/sister (n)

leisure time
accompany (v)
arrange (v)
arrangement (n)
be into something (v)
celebrate (v)

chat (v)
chat (n)
chatting (v)
compromise (v)
conversation (n)
Facebook (n)
form (a band) (v)
get-together (n)
have a laugh (v)
invite (v)
keep in touch (v)
make jokes about (v)
Messenger (n)
network (n)
noise (n)
pocket money (n)
relax (v)
rest (v)
rollerblade (v)
skate (v)
sleep over (v)
social networking site (n)
socialise (v)
waste (v)

life stages
adopt (v)
divorce (v)
inherit (v)
look after (v)
marry (v)
move into (v)
old people's home (n)
take care of (v)

relationships
arguments (n)
accept (v)
acquaintances (n)
annoying (adj)
argue (v)
close (friend) (adj)
conflict (n)
couple (n)
criticise (v)
drive someone mad (v)
end a relationship (v)
engagement (n)

ex-boy/girlfriend (n)
fall out (v)
flatmate (n)
flatmates (n)
get involved (v)
get on with (v)
get to know (v)
go out with (v)
long-lost (adj)
lose contact (v)
make fun of (v)
mate (n)
moan (v)
nag (v)
next-door neighbour (n)
old school friend (n)
pet (n)
propose (marriage) (v)
(have a good) relationship (n)
relationship (n)
separated (adj)
split up (v)
spoilt (adj)
stay in contact (v)
stranger (n)

food

cooking
baked (adj)
balanced diet (n)
blend (v)
boiled (adj)
bowl (n)
charcoal (n)
chop (v)
cook (v)
cookbook (n)
covered (v)
dish (n)
electric blender (n)
filling (n)
folded (adj)
fried (adj)
fuel (n)
gram (n)

grill (v)
grilled (adj)
instructions (n)
kilo (n)
melt (v)
mix (v)
modern (adj)
packaging (n)
pan (n)
peel (v)
pour (v)
prepare (v)
recipe (n)
rich (adj)
roasted (adj)
serve (n)
slice (v)
spread (= cover) (v)
vegan (n)

describing food and drink
crispy (adj)
delicious (adj)
disgusting (adj)
fairtrade (adj)
fast food (n)
savoury (adj)
sour (adj)
speciality (n)
spicy (adj)
sweet (adj)
taste (n)
tasty (adj)
tender (adj)
treat (n)

food items
alcohol (n)
banana (n)
beans (n)
beer (n)
burger (n)
caffeine (n)
chocolate (n)
cone (n)
crisps (n)
fizzy drink (n)

French fries (n)
grated (cheese) (adj)
hot dog (n)
ingredient (n)
juice (n)
lettuce (n)
mayonnaise (n)
noodle (n)
oil (n)
pancake (n)
pie (n)
pizza (n)
protein (n)
rum (n)
salt (n)
smoothie (n)
snack (n)
soup (n)
sour cream (n)

health

healthcare and treatment
bandage (n)
cream (n)
cure (v)
drug (n)
emergency (n)
first aid (n)
ice (n)
medicine (n)
painkiller (n)
patient (n)
penicillin (n)
plaster (n)
stitches (n)
treatment (n)
vaccine (n)

healthy/unhealthy lifestyle
carbohydrates (n)
cycling (v)
diet (n)
exercise (n)
fat (n)
fit (n)

gym (n)
health (n)
healthier (adj)
healthily (adv)
healthy (adj)
lifestyle (n)
lose weight (v)
nutrition (n)
nutritious (adj)
put on weight (v)
relax (v)
slim (adj)
unfit (adj)
vitamins (n)
weighed (v)
weight (n)

illness/injury
accident (n)
bang your head (v)
bite (v)
bleed (v)
blood pressure (n)
burn (v)
concussion (n)
cut (n)
cut yourself (v)
diseases (n)
(skin) disease (n)
dizzy (adj)
feel sick (adj)
headache (n)
headache (n)
hit (v)
hurt (v)
sick (adj)
sprain (v)
swell (v)
symptom (n)

parts of the body
ankle (n)
fibre (n)
heart (n)
liver (n)
skin (n)
throat (n)

house

describing a house
apartment block (n)
curve (n)
detached (adj)
flat (adj)
overlooks (adj)
semi-detached (adj)
strange (adj)
style (n)
traditional (adj)
unusual (adj)
weird (adj)

furniture and features
attic (n)
balcony (n)
basement (n)
bench (n)
ceiling (n)
central heating (n)
chimney (n)
cushion (n)
downstairs (n)
drawers (n)
fabric (n)
first floor (n)
ground floor (n)
handle (n)
loft (n)
loo (n)
radiator (n)
roof (n)
sheet (n)
sofa (n)
stairs (n)
storey (n)
terrace (n)
umbrella (n)
upstairs (n)
wallpaper (n)

housework
chores (n)
budget (n)
decorate (v)
have a clear out (v)
paint (v)

storing (v)
sweep (v)
tidy up (v)

natural environment

animals
frog (n)
goldfish (n)
howl (v)
lamb (n)
mosquito (n)
peacock (n)
shark (n)
whale (n)
wild (adj)
wildlife (n)
wolf (n)

environmental issues
alternative (n)
carbon (dioxide) emissions (n)
carbon dioxide (n)
carbon footprint (n)
damage (v)
destroy (v)
disaster (n)
dispose of (v)
electricity (v)
endangered (adj)
energy (n)
energy-saving (adj)
environment (n)
environmentally-friendly (adj)
extinct (adj)
freeze (v)
fuel (n)
global warming (adj)
'green' (adj)
light bulb (n)
litter (v)
melt (v)
planet (n)
pollution (n)
produce (v)
protect (v)

recycle (v)

reduce (v)

resource (n)

rubbish (n)

save (v)

throw away (v)

landscape

altitude (n)

coast (n)

desert island (n)

jungle (adj)

lake (n)

remote (n)

wave (n)

wave (n)

wood (adj)

people

appearance

bald (adj)

blonde (n)

bright blue (n)

earring (adj)

elegant (adj)

facial expression (n)

fair (n)

freckles (adj)

girly (adj)

glamorous (adj)

headband (n)

light (brown) (adj)

make-up (n)

medium-length (hair) (adj)

nails (n)

pierce (v)

plump (adj)

resemble (v)

round (adj)

scruffy (adj)

slim (adj)

straight (hair) (adj)

tall (adj)

tattoo (n)

underwear (n)

wavy (hair) (adj)

describing people

ambitious (adj)

argument (n)

billionaire (n)

celebrity (n)

deaf (adj)

divorced (adj)

heiress (n)

heroine (n)

ignore (v)

lad (n)

lucky (adj)

millionaire (n)

nasty (adj)

quadruplets (n)

residents (n)

show emotion (v)

sleepwalk (v)

snore (v)

sporty (adj)

star (n)

stranger (n)

survive (v)

tidy (adj)

typical (adj)

untidy (adj)

wealthy (adj)

well-known (adj)

emotions and feelings

admire (v)

angry (adj)

annoyed (adj)

attitude (n)

bored (adj)

can't stand (v)

complain (v)

concern (n)

delighted (adj)

depressed (adj)

desperate (adj)

disappointed (adj)

(don't) mind (v)

embarrassed (adj)

(quite) enjoy (v)

excited (adj)

excitement (n)

exhausted (adj)

find boring (adv)

frightened (adj)

furious (adj)

glad (adj)

guilty (adj)

hate (v)

heartbroken (adj)

horrified (adj)

interested (adj)

jealous (adj)

keen (adj)

lonely (adj)

love (doing something) (v)

miserable (adj)

mood (n)

nervous (adj)

passionate (adj)

pity (n)

proud (adj)

regret (v)

respect (v)

scared (adj)

shocked (adj)

sympathise (v)

upset (adj)

worried (adj)

life stages

grow up (v)

in her teens (adj)

in his twenties/thirties etc. (adj)

mature (adj)

middle-aged (adj)

(a) middle child (n)

(an) only child (n)

teenager (n)

tomboy (n)

personal qualities

annoying (adj)

argumentative (adj)

artistic (adj)

bossy (adj)

brave (adj)

calm (adj)

careful (adj)

cheeky (adj)

compassion (n)

confident (adj)
conscientious (adj)
courage (n)
crazy (adj)
dark (adj)
determined (adj)
dominant (adj)
dynamic (adj)
easy-going (adj)
friendly (adj)
fussy (adj)
generous (adj)
genius (n)
hard-working (adj)
indecisive (adj)
insensitive (adj)
inspiration (n)
intelligent (adj)
kind (adj)
kindness (n)
leader   (n)
leadership (n)
loud (adj)
melodramatic (adj)
nice (adj)
nosy (adj)
organised (adj)
outgoing (adj)
patient (adj)
personality (n)
polite (adj)
popular (n)
pro-active (adj)
punctual (adj)
quiet (adj)
reliable (adj)
rude (adj)
self-centred (adj)
selfish (adj)
sensitive (adj)
shy (adj)
skills (n)
smart (adj)
sociable (adj)
spoilt (adj)
strong (personality) (adj)
sympathetic (adj)

talented (adj)
talkative (adj)
tidy (adj)
weak (adj)

social interaction/activity
apologise (v)
behave (v)
come over (v)
complain (adv)
concentrating (v)
discipline (n)
(smiling from) ear to ear (n)
fight (v)
gossip (n)
greetings (n)
introduce yourself (v)
meet (v)
respond (v)
shout (v)
strangers (n)
support (n)

school

at school
break (n)
chalk (n)
gap year (n)
glue stick (n)
notice board (n)
routine (n)
rules (n)
school bag (n)
scissors (n)
strict (adj)
subjects (n)
(wear) a uniform (n)
workspace (n)

learning and exams
achievement (n)
attention span (n)
challenge (n)
compulsory (adj)
concentrate (v)
concentration (n)

coursework (n)
discipline (n)
distraction (n)
do well in something (v)
educate (v)
educational (adj)
essay (n)
fail an exam (v)
get good marks (v)
goal(s) (n)
grades (n)
improve (v)
improvement (n)
knowledge (n)
learn (v)
lecture (n)
optional (adjv)
pass an exam (n)
qualifications (n)
revise (v)
specialise (v)
start school (v)

people and places
bully (n)
classmate (n)
head teacher (n)
mixed school (n)
private school (n)
pupils (n)
secondary school (n)
single-sex school (n)
staff (n)
state school (adj)

science and technology

describing and/or using science and technology
computer-generated (adj)
crane (n)
creation (n)
development (n)
endurance (n)
experiment (n)
generation (n)

indestructible (adj)
intend (v)
metal (n)
optical illusion (n)
primitive (adj)
revolutionary (adj)
spark (n)

technology
antibiotics (n)
car manufacturing (n)
cell phone (n)
computer chip (n)
copper (n)
device (n)
discovery (n)
electronic (adj)
graphics (n)
gunpowder (n)
information (n)
invention (n)
inventor (n)
lifeboat (n)
mobile phone (n)
online (adj)
power lines (n)
printing press (n)
robot (n)
rocket (n)
science fiction (n)
sign (n)
speaker (n)
switch (n)
telephone (n)
two-seater plane (n)
wheel (n)
wire (n)
World Wide Web (n)

useful verbs
assemble (v)
catch on (v)
crash (v)
delete (v)
design (v)
develop (v)
discover (v)
hack into (v)

invent (v)
march   (v)
replace (v)
rescue (v)
set out (v)
solve (v)
switch off/on (v)
turn down/up (v)

shopping and services

goods
dye (v)
leather (n)
purse (n)
wallet (n)
wax (n)

selling/buying
advert(isement) (n)
advertise (v)
advice (n)
boutique shop (n)
chain (n)
cheap (adj)
clothes catalogue (adj)
customers (n)
cutting (v)
enquire (v)
expensive (adj)
kiosk (n)
queue (n)
queueing (v)
retail sales (n)
serve (drinks) (v)
shopping trolley (n)
valuable (adj)
(to be) worth (adj)

sport

equipment and places
bat (n)
club (n)
competitive (n)

crash helmet (n)
dressing room (n)
goggles (n)
gym (n)
racquet (n)
rubber (n)
saddle (n)
scoreboard (n)
skateboard (n)
stadium (n)
stopwatch (n)
surf board (n)
whistle (n)

sports events
athletics (v)
beat (v)
break a record (v)
comment (v)
compete (v)
competition (n)
crossing (v)
goal (n)
match (n)
medal (n)
race (v)
score (v)
support (v)
support (n)
title (n)
trophy (n)
venue (n)
win a match (v)
world record (n)

sports people
athlete (n)
champion (n)
coach (n)
defender (n)
fans (n)
instructor (n)
opponent (n)
referee (n)
striker (n)
team (n)
team mate (n)

training and exercise
black belt (n)
blow (v)
dive (v)
enter (v)
get changed (v)
get fit (v)
go running (v)
injured (adj)
injuries (n)
kick (v)
lose (v)
squad (n)

types of sport
basketball (n)
gymnastics (n)
martial arts (n)
sailing (n)
table tennis (n)
Taekwondo (n)
training (n)

travelling and tourism

describing holiday locations
area (n)
awesome (adj)
coast (n)
destination (n)
eco-friendly (adj)
exotic (adj)
green (adj)
landmark (n)
luxury (adj)
remote (adj)
scenery (n)

holidays
abroad (adv)
abroad (n)
amusement park (n)
camp (n)
camping (v)
culture (n)
directions (n)

foreigner (n)
guided tour (n)
historic (adj)
island (n)
journey (n)
local (adj)
location (n)
main square (n)
monument (n)
pack up (v)
sanctuary (n)
sightseeing (v)
staying (in the US) (v)
tent (n)
trip (n)
tropical (adj)
vacation (n)
visitor (n)

means of transport
airship (n)
crafts (n)
cruise ship (n)
cycle (v)
cycle lane (n)
distance (n)
driver's licence (n)
motorway (n)
parachute (n)
port (n)
public transport (n)
ship (n)

problems and accidents
cancelled (v)
crowded (adj)
delayed (n)
get stuck (v)
noisy (adj)
rescue (v)
sink (v)
traffic (n)
traffic jam (n)
unreliable (adj)

transport
abandon (v)
arrive (v)

bus pass (n)
compartment (n)
drive (v)
driving test (n)
freeway (n)
fuel (n)
journey (n)
limousine (n)
motorbike (n)
passenger (n)
passer-by (n)
pavement (n)
pick someone up (v)
ride (v)
roadside (n)
route (n)
runway (n)
rush hour (n)
sign (n)
step into the road (v)
van (n)

work

at work
abilities (n)
apply (v)
carry (v)
clarification (n)
colleague (n)
crew (n)
export (n)
get the sack (v)
(long) hours (n)
job satisfaction (n)
placard (n)
place (v)
promotion (n)
replace (v)
set goals (v)
solution (n)
strike (n)
take control (v)
take over (v)
task (n)
working conditions (n)

describing jobs and skills

applicant (n)
build (n)
business (n)
call centre (n)
career (n)
career opportunities (n)
challenging (adj)
factory (n)
full-time (adj)
fun (adj)
hazardous (adj)
interview (n)
join (the army) (v)
key (to success) (n)
level (n)
outdoor (adj)
part-time (adj)
profession (n)
repair (v)
repetitive (adj)
respectable (adj)
retired (adj)
rewarding (adj)
stand still (n)
stressful (adj)
strict (adj)
tiring (adj)
unemployed (adj)
useful (adj)
well-treated (adj)
work permit (n)

jobs

apprenticeship (n)
advertising executive (n)
analyst (n)
architect (n)
beautician (n)
cobbler (n)
consultant (n)
correspondent (n)
dry cleaner (n)
editor (n)
employer (n)
examiner (n)
expert (n)
explorer (n)
firefighter (n)
fisherman (n)
gardener (n)
governess (n)
jeweller (n)
journalist (n)
(farm) labourer (n)
make your fortune (v)
manager (n)
(coal) mine (n)
miner (n)
model (n)
optician (n)
personal assistant (n)
photo shoot (n)
psychologist (n)
public relations (n)

receptionist (n)
reporter (n)
riot police (n)
sailor (n)
servant (n)
social worker (n)
supervisor (n)
(game) tester (n)
voluntary work (n)
volunteer (n)

money

badly-paid (adj)
earn (v)
earn one's living (v)
fortune (n)
minimum wage (n)
pay rise (n)
salary (n)
wages (n)
well-paid (adj)

skills and qualities

achievement (n)
ambition (n)
charity work (n)
experience (n)
graduate (v)
responsibilities (n)
skills (n)
solve (v)
successful (adj)

functions list

Greeting, meeting and getting to know people

Greeting/Introducing yourself
Excuse me …/Hello!
Let me introduce myself, I'm Adam Brown.
Nice/Pleased to meet you.
My name's …/I'm …

Showing interest
Really?/Seriously?
That's amazing!
Wow!/Cool!

Asking for repetition/clarification
Sorry?
What was that?
What do you mean?

Asking polite questions
Which part of Italy do you come from?
How long have you been living in England?
What do you do for a living?
How long have you been working abroad?
Do you have a family?

Asking for information
When did you start playing tennis?
How did you become interested in it?
What is your daily training routine?
Have you won any competitions or medals?

Have you broken any records?
Have you ever had any injuries?
What are your hopes for the future?

Responding politely
And how about you?
Really, how interesting!
Sorry, I didn't catch what you said.

Opinions

Giving and explaining your opinion
Personally I (don't) think …
I (definitely) think he should …
(Obviously) you shouldn't …
It's (not) fair that …
(She's) completely right.
I think (he's) wrong because …
I (don't) feel sorry for them because …
She probably feels that …
Personally I'd …
In that situation, I wouldn't …
We've decided it is best because …
We don't think it is suitable because …

Asking other people's opinion
Do you think (this punishment is fair)?
Do you feel sorry for (them)?
What would you do in that situation?
What do you think of …

Talking about art
I really like the style.
It's very beautiful/original/sad.
I don't understand what the artist is trying to say.
I think it's ugly/ridiculous.
It makes you think.
It doesn't mean anything to me!
I don't think it's a work of art.
It reminds me of wallpaper.
What do you think the artist is trying to say?
Do you think this is a work of art?

Directions

Asking for directions
Excuse me …
How do I get to the Scott Monument/there?
Do you know …?
I'm looking for …

Giving directions
At the traffic lights, turn left.
Cross the street, opposite the bank.
It's five minutes from here.
It's just there/next to/opposite the station.
Go past the castle/and then/straight on until you get to the bridge.

Apologising/responding to an apology
Sorry I couldn't help.
No problem. Thanks anyway.

Thanking/responding to thanks

Thank you./Thanks very much.

You're welcome.

Descriptions

Describing dishes

It's a kind of pie/pancake/soup.

The main ingredients are fish and rice.

The potatoes are grilled/boiled/fried.

It tastes spicy/sour.

It's sold at kiosks.

It's usually eaten at home.

People eat it for lunch in the winter.

Asking about typical dishes

Have you tried harira yet?

What's it made of?

How is it cooked?

What does it taste like?

Where is it sold?

When is it usually eaten?

Responding with interest

It sounds delicious/interesting/nice!

I'd like to try it!

Describing buildings

It's painted bright colours.

The balcony is curved.

It's a two-storey house.

The chimney's in the middle.

There's a balcony on the first floor.

It looks very unusual.

It's probably quite small inside.

The balcony overlooks the park.

Asking about buildings

What kind of house is it?

What colour is it painted?

How big is it?

Is there a chimney?

Does it have any other unusual features?

Describing objects

It's made of plastic.

It's got speakers.

It's for measuring things.

It's about 30cm long.

It's long and thin.

Asking about objects

How big is it?

What shape is it?

What is it made of?

What's it used for?

Has it got any special features?

Suggestions

Making suggestions

What/How about going to the cinema ?

What do you think of these trousers ?

Disagreeing with suggestions

I'm not sure about that.

I like the idea but we could try this other one.

It's not bad but I think we can do better.

Agreeing with suggestions

I think it's a good idea.

That's it! I love it!

I suppose so.

Well, all right, that will be fine.

Making an alternative suggestion

Here's another idea – we can sing a rock song.

I've got a better idea.

Asking for agreement

Do we all agree?

Request and offers

Making a request

Can you put it over there?

Would you mind getting my saxophone?

Could you move those chairs?

Responding to a request

Yes/Sure, no problem/okay./Yes, all right.

Making an offer

Shall I put it over here?

Do you want me to do something?

Responding to an offer

Yes, please./No, it's all right.

Thanking

Thanks a lot.

That's very kind of you.

Arrangements

Starting a conversation

Hi!

What's new?

What are you doing on Saturday?

Inviting someone

How about going out somewhere?

Do you fancy coming to the gig?

Why don't we go out on Sunday?

Accepting an invitation

Sounds good/great.

Sure, why not?

That would be great!

Refusing an invitation

I'm sorry, I can't.

I'm busy.

I'd love to, but I have plans.

That's a good idea but I'm on holiday that week.

Advice

Asking what's wrong
What's the matter?
What's the problem?
What's up?

Asking for advice
Can I ask your opinion about something?
What do you think we should do?
Should I say something?

Giving advice
I wouldn't say anything about that.
You should try something different.
I think you should speak to him.

Agreeing/responding sympathetically
You're right.
Sure!
Absolutely!
Exactly!

Notes

1 Making suggestions

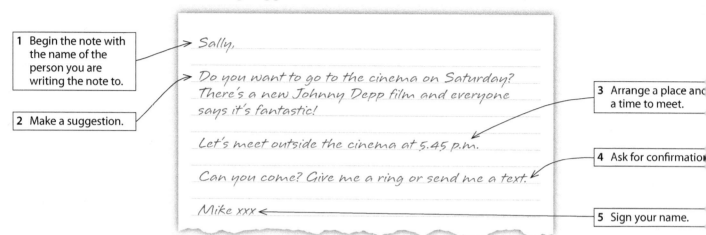

1 Begin the note with the name of the person you are writing the note to.

2 Make a suggestion.

> Sally,
>
> Do you want to go to the cinema on Saturday? There's a new Johnny Depp film and everyone says it's fantastic!
>
> Let's meet outside the cinema at 5.45 p.m.
>
> Can you come? Give me a ring or send me a text.
>
> Mike xxx

3 Arrange a place and a time to meet.

4 Ask for confirmation

5 Sign your name.

2 Asking to do something

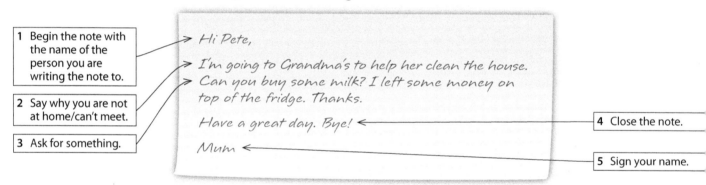

1 Begin the note with the name of the person you are writing the note to.

2 Say why you are not at home/can't meet.

3 Ask for something.

> Hi Pete,
>
> I'm going to Grandma's to help her clean the house. Can you buy some milk? I left some money on top of the fridge. Thanks.
>
> Have a great day. Bye!
>
> Mum

4 Close the note.

5 Sign your name.

Useful language

Making suggestions

Let's go to the cinema/watch a DVD/go to the park.

Do you want to come/meet me?

Come to the park/for a coffee!

Come and join us!

What about tomorrow/next week?

What about meeting later/having pizza?

Have you got time at the weekend/on Friday?

Arranging a place

See you at/outside …

The/My address is …

Here's a map …

The cinema is in …

Let's meet at my house/at the café.

Arranging a time

Let's meet at 2 p.m. /after school.

See you at 5 p.m.

Asking for confirmation

Can you come?

Send me a text.

Give me a call.

Saying why you are not at home/can't meet

I'm going out because …

I'm going to …

I can't go out tonight because … Sorry!

I'm going to my cousin's/seeing Kevin, so I can't meet.

Asking to do something

Can you bring a DVD/buy some bread?

Do you mind bringing a DVD/buying some bread?

Closing a note

See you soon,

See you in the afternoon/in the evening.

Have a good day.

Bye!

Love,

Postcard

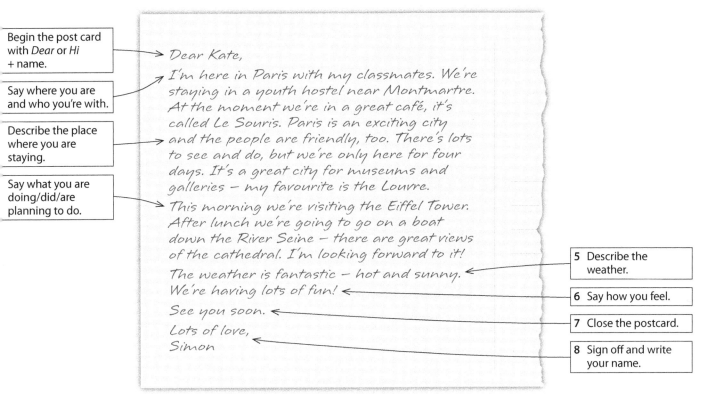

Begin the post card with *Dear* or *Hi* + name.

Say where you are and who you're with.

Describe the place where you are staying.

Say what you are doing/did/are planning to do.

Dear Kate,

I'm here in Paris with my classmates. We're staying in a youth hostel near Montmartre. At the moment we're in a great café, it's called Le Souris. Paris is an exciting city and the people are friendly, too. There's lots to see and do, but we're only here for four days. It's a great city for museums and galleries — my favourite is the Louvre.

This morning we're visiting the Eiffel Tower. After lunch we're going to go on a boat down the River Seine — there are great views of the cathedral. I'm looking forward to it!

The weather is fantastic — hot and sunny. We're having lots of fun!

See you soon.

Lots of love,
Simon

5 Describe the weather.

6 Say how you feel.

7 Close the postcard.

8 Sign off and write your name.

Useful language

Beginning a postcard

Hi,/Dear Anna,

I hope you're okay. / I hope you're well.

How's things?

Saying where you are/who you're with

I'm in Warsaw.

I've just arrived at …

I'm spending my holiday/weekend …

I'm on a school trip in …

I'm with my friends.

I'm here with my family.

I'm in London with my classmates.

Describing a place

There is/are …

My favourite shop/place is …

The shops/restaurants/cafés/museums are … interesting/expensive/great/fantastic …

The city is exciting/fantastic/brilliant/boring/polluted.

There's a lot to see and do.

It's a great city/place for …

Places: galleries, museums, beach, forest, amusement park, old town, park, castle, shops

Accommodation

We're staying in a hotel/guest house/campsite.

I'm staying with friends.

Saying what you are doing/did/are going to do

At the moment, I'm sitting in a café.

Today we're visiting museums/relaxing/ sitting on the beach.

Yesterday we visited a museum/went to the beach/ did some sightseeing.

Tomorrow we're going to go skiing/relax/ explore the city centre.

This evening I'm going to a restaurant/concert/ on a coach trip.

Activities: sailing, windsurfing, snorkelling, climbing, skiing, sunbathing, shopping, sightseeing, walking

Describing the weather

It's sunny/rainy/windy/snowy.

It's hot/warm/cold/freezing.

The weather is great/terrible/okay.

Saying how you feel

We're having a great/terrible time.

I'm having lots of fun.

Closing a postcard

See you soon,

Bye for now!

Signing off

Lots of love,

Take care,

Best wishes,

Love,

Notices

1 Lost items

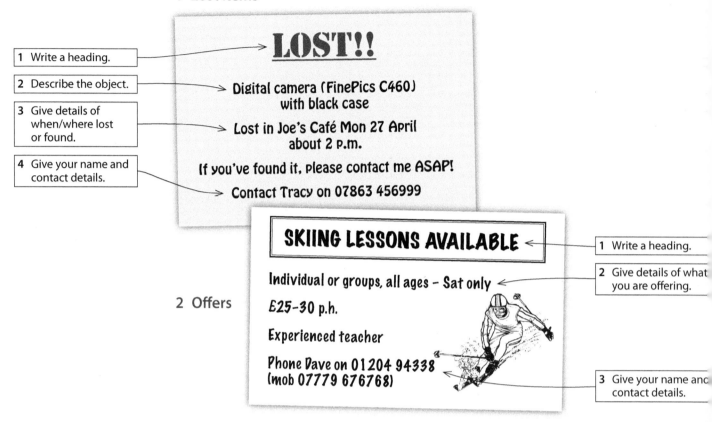

1	Write a heading.
2	Describe the object.
3	Give details of when/where lost or found.
4	Give your name and contact details.

LOST!!

Digital camera (FinePics C460) with black case

Lost in Joe's Café Mon 27 April about 2 p.m.

If you've found it, please contact me ASAP!

Contact Tracy on 07863 456999

2 Offers

SKIING LESSONS AVAILABLE

Individual or groups, all ages – Sat only

£25–30 p.h.

Experienced teacher

Phone Dave on 01204 94338 (mob 07779 676768)

1	Write a heading.
2	Give details of what you are offering.
3	Give your name and contact details.

Useful language

Headings
Lost!
Found!
Wanted!
Guitar/Snowboarding/French lessons available
Trip to Paris/London
Room for rent
For sale

Describing something
It's a mobile/camera …
It's a silver watch/small black dog …
It's got stickers on/a black case …

Saying where/when lost or found
I left it at the gym/café.
I lost/found it at the sports centre.
I lost/found it on Sat a.m./around 3.00/on 5 May.

Giving details of offers
£10 reward!
2 tickets for Muse concert, only £15 each
Experienced teacher – classes for all ages
Individual or small groups – eves and wknds only
Room for rent – £60 p.w.
Trip to London on 24 August

Giving contact details
Phone/Call/Contact Mark on 346 7789 …
Please contact/call/phone Jan on …
Send me an email to Kate at …
Text me on …
If you've found it, please call Sally. My mobile is …

Abbreviations
Mon (Monday), Tues (Tuesday), Weds (Wednesday), Thurs (Thursday), Fri (Friday), Sat (Saturday), Sun (Sunday)
a.s.a.p./ASAP (as soon as possible)
pls (please)
N/S (non-smoker)
mins (minutes)
mob (mobile)
yr old (year-old)
p.w. (per week)
p.h. (per hour)
wknds (weekends)
eves (evenings)
a.m. (morning)
p.m. (afternoon/evening)

Invitations

Give the invitation a title. → DISCOVER SPAIN

Make an invitation. → Please come to the Discover Spain afternoon

Give a reason. → The school Spanish Club are holding an afternoon to learn all about Spain.

Don't miss the chance to try traditional Spanish food, drinks and dancing

Bring your friends and family!

On Friday 23 March at 7.30 p.m. in the school hall

If you are interested, contact Alex in class 4B

RSVP

4 Give further details.

5 Give the date, the time and the place.

6 Ask for a reply to the invitation and give a contact name, number or email.

Useful language

Giving a title
Fancy dress/Halloween party!

Come to a party!

Farewell Mrs Evans

Celebrate the end of the exams!

Happy birthday!

School concert

Inviting people
Please come to …

We'd like to invite you to …

I'm having a birthday party …

We request the pleasure of your company (= we'd like to invite you) …

I'd really love it if you could come.

Saying where and when
In the school hall/town square …

On Saturday 5 June …

At 2.30 p.m. …

From 8 till 12 at the Star Café …

Giving a reason
A party to celebrate …

An evening to learn about …

A party to say farewell to …

A welcome party for …

Giving further details
Live music and dancing

Please bring drinks

Bring your family and friends!

With drinks, food and dancing!

Casual dress

We're going out for a meal after the concert

I'm singing in the concert/performing/in the play

Asking for a reply
If you want to come, contact …

If you are interested, call …,

RSVP (= French for 'Please reply')

RSVP The School Secretary

Please call me if you can come/make it.

A personal letter

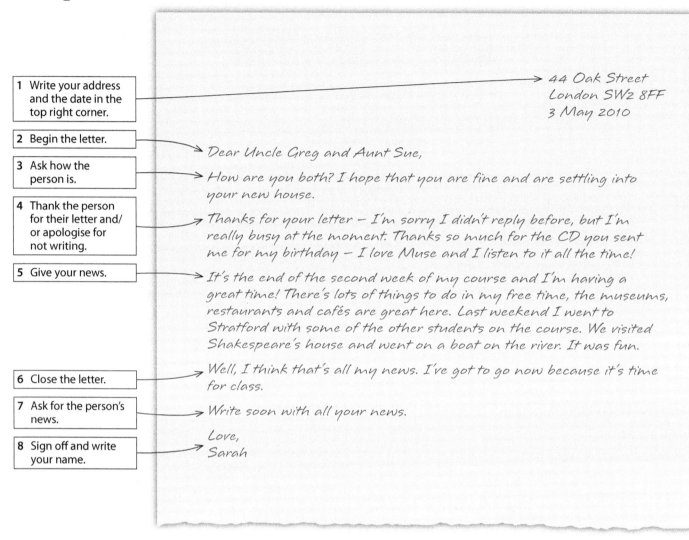

1 Write your address and the date in the top right corner.

2 Begin the letter.

3 Ask how the person is.

4 Thank the person for their letter and/or apologise for not writing.

5 Give your news.

6 Close the letter.

7 Ask for the person's news.

8 Sign off and write your name.

44 Oak Street
London SW2 8FF
3 May 2010

Dear Uncle Greg and Aunt Sue,

How are you both? I hope that you are fine and are settling into your new house.

Thanks for your letter — I'm sorry I didn't reply before, but I'm really busy at the moment. Thanks so much for the CD you sent me for my birthday — I love Muse and I listen to it all the time!

It's the end of the second week of my course and I'm having a great time! There's lots of things to do in my free time, the museums, restaurants and cafés are great here. Last weekend I went to Stratford with some of the other students on the course. We visited Shakespeare's house and went on a boat on the river. It was fun.

Well, I think that's all my news. I've got to go now because it's time for class.

Write soon with all your news.

Love,
Sarah

Useful language

Beginning a personal letter
Dear Kate,
Hi Kate,
Dear Grandma/Uncle Jack,

Asking how someone is
How are you?
How are you doing?
I hope you are well/fine.
How are things?

Thanking
Thanks for your letter/card …
It was good to hear from you.
Thank you for your letter/the cheque/the book you sent …
I'm writing to thank you for …
It was really kind of you to …
Thank you very much …

Apologising for not writing
Sorry I haven't written/replied before, but …
Sorry I haven't been in touch, but …
I'm really sorry that …
Sorry for not replying/writing …
Apologies for not writing sooner/forgetting your birthday …

Inviting
Would you like to …
We're having a party on …
I hope you'll be able to come/join us …
I'm writing to invite you to …
I'd love it if you could come …

Giving your news
I'm writing to tell you …
My latest news is …
Last weekend I …
I'm having a great time in …

Closing a personal letter
Well, I think that's everything/all my news …
So that's my news.
I hope all is well with you.
I've got to go now because …
Say hello to …

Asking for someone's news
I'd love to hear all your news.
What's your news?
So that's my news. What about you?
Write soon and tell me your news.

Signing off
Lots of love,	Take care,
Love,	See you soon!
All the best,	Give my love to …
All my love,	Bye for now,
Best wishes,	Write soon,

A letter from a reader

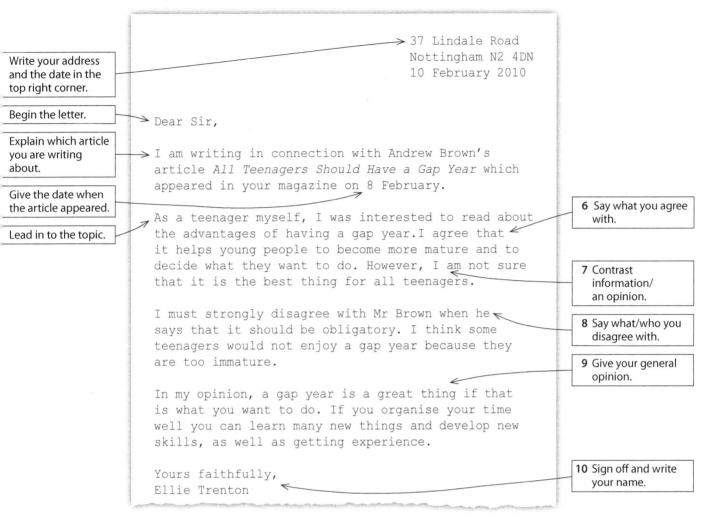

Write your address and the date in the top right corner. → 37 Lindale Road
Nottingham N2 4DN
10 February 2010

Begin the letter. → Dear Sir,

Explain which article you are writing about. → I am writing in connection with Andrew Brown's article *All Teenagers Should Have a Gap Year* which appeared in your magazine on 8 February.

Give the date when the article appeared.

Lead in to the topic. → As a teenager myself, I was interested to read about the advantages of having a gap year. I agree that it helps young people to become more mature and to decide what they want to do. However, I am not sure that it is the best thing for all teenagers.

6 Say what you agree with.

7 Contrast information/an opinion.

I must strongly disagree with Mr Brown when he says that it should be obligatory. I think some teenagers would not enjoy a gap year because they are too immature.

8 Say what/who you disagree with.

9 Give your general opinion.

In my opinion, a gap year is a great thing if that is what you want to do. If you organise your time well you can learn many new things and develop new skills, as well as getting experience.

Yours faithfully,
Ellie Trenton

10 Sign off and write your name.

Useful language

Beginning a formal letter
Dear Sir,
Dear Editor,
Dear Sir or Madam,
Dear + name,

Explaining your reason for writing
I am writing in connection with (+ title) …
I have just read your article (+ title) …
I am writing about the article/report/editorial …

Saying where/when you saw the article
… which appeared in the paper on 6 January.
… which was in last Friday's paper/last month's magazine.

Leading into the topic
As a (teenager/writer/student) myself, I …
I would like to thank you for/
congratulate you on the article.
The article was very interesting because …
I found the article very interesting/informative …
I was surprised/shocked to read that …

Saying you agree
I agree with (Mr Brown)/that …
I completely agree …
I could not agree more with (the writer)/that …
I agree that it is true that …

Contrasting an opinion
However, …
On the other hand, …

Saying you disagree
I do not agree that …
I disagree with (Mr Brown)/that …
I strongly disagree …

Giving your opinion
In my opinion, …
I think that …
I believe that …
It seems to me that …

Signing off
Yours faithfully, (if the letter starts *Dear Sir/Madam*)
Yours sincerely, (if the letter starts *Dear* + name)

A letter of complaint

1 Write your address and the date in the top right corner.

2 Write the name and address of the company you are writing to on the left.

3 Begin the letter.

4 In **paragraph 1**, give your reason/s for writing.

5 In **paragraph 2**, explain the problem in detail.

29 Mill Lane
Brighton BR2 3RF
6 January 2010

Customer Services
JD Stores,
6 Rydal Road,
London NW3 2JM

Dear Mr Davison,

I am writing to make a complaint about a watch that I bought from JD Stores on 28 December.

There are two problems with the watch. Firstly, the battery stopped working after only a few days. However, the information leaflet says the battery should last for one to two years. Secondly, there is a fault with the glass and it is difficult to read the numbers properly. The model I looked at in the shop was fine, so I was surprised that the watch I bought was not the same. I took the watch back to the store, but the manager told me I had to contact you directly.

I am enclosing a copy of the receipt. Could you please send me a new watch or give me a refund as soon as possible?

I look forward to hearing from you.

Yours sincerely,

Christine Brown

Christine Brown

6 In **paragraph 3**, say what you want to happen as a result of your letter.

7 Say that you expect a reply.

8 Sign off and write your name.

9 Print your name underneath or write it in CAPITAL LETTERS.

Useful language

Beginning a formal letter
Dear Sir or Madam,
Dear Mr Brown,/Ms Jones,

Saying why you are writing
I am writing to complain about …
I am writing to make a complaint about …
I am writing about a fault in a camera/TV/phone.
I am writing about a problem with my course/hotel reservation/holiday.

Giving details
I bought it/them from JD Stores on 28 December.
I bought a watch/mobile phone/dress at your store yesterday.
I visited your restaurant last week.
I started a course at your language school ten days ago.

Describing problems
The battery does not work.
There is a problem with the remote control.
It is impossible to use the phone camera.

There is a fault in the controls.
It broke two days after I bought it.
We had a terrible meal because …
The remote control was missing.
The TV suddenly stopped working.
The course is very disorganised.
The room was very noisy/dirty and the service was slow/terrible.

Saying what you expect
Could you please send me …
I would like a refund/replacement.
I enclose a copy of the receipt.
I would be grateful if you could repair the camera/phone/watch.

Showing you expect a reply
I look forward to hearing from you in the near future.
I look forward to hearing from you as soon as possible.
I look forward to your prompt response.

Signing off
Yours sincerely, (if the letter starts *Dear* + name)
Yours faithfully, (if the letter starts *Dear Sir/Madam*)

irregular verbs

Infinitive	2nd Form (Past Simple)	3rd Form (Past Participle)
be	was/were	been
become	became	become
begin	began	begun
break	broke	broken
bring	brought	brought
build	built	built
burn	burned/burnt	burned/burnt
buy	bought	bought
catch	caught	caught
choose	chose	chosen
come	came	come
cost	cost	cost
cut	cut	cut
dig	dug	dug
do	did	done
draw	drew	drawn
dream	dreamed/dreamt	dreamed/dreamt
drink	drank	drunk
drive	drove	driven
eat	ate	eaten
fall	fell	fallen
feed	fed	fed
feel	felt	felt
fight	fought	fought
find	found	found
fly	flew	flown
forget	forgot	forgotten
forgive	forgave	forgiven
get	got	got
give	gave	given
go	went	gone
grow	grew	grown
have	had	had
hear	heard	heard
hide	hid	hidden
hit	hit	hit
hold	held	held
hurt	hurt	hurt
keep	kept	kept
know	knew	known
lead	led	led
learn	learned/learnt	learned/learnt
leave	left	left

Infinitive	2nd Form (Past Simple)	3rd Form (Past Participle)
let	let	let
lie	lay	lain
light	lit	lit
lose	lost	lost
make	made	made
mean	meant	meant
meet	met	met
pay	paid	paid
put	put	put
read /riːd/	read /red/	read /red/
ride	rode	ridden
ring	rang	rung
run	ran	run
say	said	said
see	saw	seen
sell	sold	sold
send	sent	sent
set	set	set
shine	shone	shone
show	showed	shown
shut	shut	shut
sing	sang	sung
sit	sat	sat
sleep	slept	slept
smell	smelled/smelt	smelled/smelt
speak	spoke	spoken
spend	spent	spent
spill	spilled/spilt	spilled/spilt
stand	stood	stood
steal	stole	stolen
swim	swam	swum
take	took	taken
teach	taught	taught
tear	tore	torn
tell	told	told
think	thought	thought
throw	threw	thrown
understand	understood	understood
wake	woke	woken
wear	wore	worn
win	won	won
write	wrote	written

answer key: self-assessment tests and exam tests

self-assessment test 1
1 2 enter, 3 a goal, 4 goals, 5 state, 6 your best, 7 revise

2 2 about, 3 rules, 4 specialise, 5 salary, 6 find, 7 career,

3 2 did they come, 3 looks, 4 haven't seen, 5 are you thinking, 6 went, 7 is getting, 8 doesn't want

4 2 This is the place where I saw her for the first time.
3 The police are looking for the woman whose fingerprints were on the gun.
4 I didn't like the meal she cooked for us yesterday.
5 A Sat-Nav is an electronic device which/that helps people to find their way.
6 I don't like teachers who give a lot of homework.

5 2 stand, 3 who/that, 4 point, 5 've, 6 degree, 7 at, 8 not

6 1 Robert, 2 Grace, 3 Ann, 4 Robert, 5 Ann

7 1 ?, 2 ✗, 3 ✓, 4 ✓, 5 ✗, 6 ?

8 2 meet, 3 Seriously, 4 mean

9 2 c, 3 b, 4 d, 5 –, 6 a, 7 e

self-assessment test 2
1 2 c, 3 a, 4 a, 5 c, 6 b, 7 b

2 2 more organised, 3 the nicest, 4 more sociable than, 5 as argumentative as, 6 the most indecisive

3 2 repetitive, 3 social, 4 full-time, 5 glamorous, 6 living, 7 shy,

4 2 had to, 3 go, 4 much, 5 don't have to, 6 from, 7 read, 8 not allowed, 9 as

5 2 challenging, 3 stressful, 4 personality, 5 ambitious, 6 rewarding

6 1 Olivia, 2 Paul, 3 David, 4 Paul, 5 Rebecca, 6 David, 7 Olivia, 8 David

7 2 'm not sure, 3 another idea, 4 all right, 5 think of, 6 not bad, 7 've got, 8 How about, 9 don't think, 10 all agree

8 1 What does she look like?,
2 What do they like?, 3 What's he like?

self-assessment test 3
1 2 footprint, 3 annoyed, 4 waste, 5 delayed, 6 turning down, 7 classmate, 8 step-

2 2 've/have known; since,
3 've/have been thinking; since,
4 's/has been learning; for,
5 Have you read, 6 was; for
7 have you been seeing

3 2 lanes, 3 team, 4 global, 5 fuel, 6 jams, 7 get

4 2 I think our new head teacher will be very strict.
3 I'll get married when I'm 25.
4 Ian's planned everything – he's going to travel next year.
5 If it doesn't stop raining, we'll stay at home.
6 I won't talk to you unless you apologise for being rude.
OR If you don't apologise for being rude, I won't talk to you.

5 2 gave, 3 nervous, 4 got on, 5 saw, 6 up, 7 unless

6 2 the South East, 3 less, 4 energy use, 5 carbon emissions, 6 online/the internet, 7 wash the/your car

7 1 c, 2 a, 3 c, 4 d, 5 b, 6 d

self-assessment test 4
1 2 c, 3 d, 4 f, 5 h, 6 a, 7 b, 8 g

2 2 serve, 3 block, 4 melts, 5 attic, 6 peel, 7 balcony

3 2 Peter's going to have his heart checked.
3 We've had a new double sink installed in our kitchen.
4 You should have your hair dyed.
5 I will have all the locks in my house changed.
6 My aunt has milk delivered to her house every day.

4 2 lost, 3 would knock, 4 didn't nag, 5 would let/'d let, 6 wouldn't make, 7 didn't feel

5 2 is still being repaired.
3 I wasn't/weren't so short./I was/were taller.
4 is spoken in many countries.
5 had enough/more money, he'd/would go on holiday to Africa.
6 have been broken in our school.
7 was invented by Auguste and Louis Lumière.

6 Dialogue 2 – I, d
Dialogue 3 – mind, a
Dialogue 4 – made, c
Dialogue 5 – What, e

7 2 reasons, 3 floor, 4 there, 5 overlooks, 6 hand, 7 opinion

8 1 E, 2 B, 3 G, 4 D, 5 A, 6 F
(C is the extra heading.)

self-assessment test 5
1 2 symptom, 3 gossip, 4 dizzy, 5 cartoon, 6 crew, 7 review, 8 media

2 2 used to go to the cinema more
3 entered the room while/when I was arguing
4 told me to put my books
5 felt sick because she'd/had eaten too
6 didn't use to fall asleep in front
7 asked (me) if I could help him with his OR asked me to help him with his

3 2 burnt, 3 eventually, 4 the swelling, 5 the news, 6 privacy

4 2 was sinking, 3 had rescued, 4 used to have/had, 5 had got, 6 would hurt

5 2 Ian asked me why I hadn't come to his birthday party.
3 Beth didn't use to be so sociable.
4 He told/said to me that he wanted to go home.
5 Rob asked us if/whether we had plans for the weekend.
6 I told her that Tom and I were going to get married.
7 I took a photo of my sister while was sleeping.
8 Their teacher asked them to stop talking.

6 1 d, 2 e, 3 g, 4 a, 5 c, 6 h, 7 f
Extra phrase = b

7 1 ✓, 2 ✗, 3 ✓, 4 ?, 5 ✗

8 2 e, 3 a, 4 c, 5 f, 6 d

9 2 Personally, 3 sorry, 4 should

self-assessment test 6
1 2 b, 3 c, 4 c, 5 a, 6 a, 7 b

2 2 stage, 3 switch, 4 object, 5 audience, 6 housework

3 2 hadn't shouted, 3 would have won, 4 'd/had invited, 5 wouldn't have been/hadn't missed

4 2 Neither, 3 getting up, 4 every, 5 Reading, 6 to study, 7 a little, 8 to revise

5 2 invention, 3 developments, 4 educate, 5 knowledge,

6 2 his face, 3 intelligence, 4 age and sex, 5 different/more/other, 6 a

7 2 background, 3 In, 4 must, 5 look/are, 6 see, 7 There, 8 reminds

8 Dialogue 1
2 shape is it, 3 has it got, 4 is it used for
Dialogue 2
5 the matter/the problem/up, 6 Can I ask your, 7 do you think, 8 should try

exam test 1
1 1 ✗, 2 ✓, 3 ?, 4 ✗, 5 ?, 6 ✓

2 1 d, 2 e, 3 a, 4 b
Extra statement = c

3 2 who, 3 educate, 4 secondary, 5 as, 6 sack, 7 degree, 8 in, 9 conditions, 10 her, 11 which

4 2 living, 3 sailor, 4 consultant, 5 ambitious, 6 scientist, 7 solution, 8 successful, 9 wealthy, 10 satisfaction, 11 unhappy

exam test 2
1 1 death, 2 sad, 3 football/ball, 4 cooking, 5 Jimmy's dad/Jimmy's father, 6 nervous, 7 jealous, 8 married, 9 step-brother, 10 surprising

2 1 c, 2 c, 3 a, 4 b, 5 b, 6 b

3 2 a, 3 a, 4 b, 5 c, 6 a, 7 c, 8 b, 9 c, 10 a, 11 b

4 2 be, 3 in, 4 all, 5 of, 6 to, 7 who/that, 8 of, 9 to, 10 about, 11 you, 12 a, 13 spend

exam test 3
1 1 c, 2 b, 3 c, 4 a, 5 a, 6 d

2 1 d, 2 e, 3 b, 4 a
Extra statement = c

3 3 a, 4 ✓, 5 has, 6 he, 7 ✓, 8 much, 9 was, 10 ✓, 11 which, 12 being

4 2 hadn't sprained, 3 to play, 4 has been found, 5 I had studied, 6 have my jacket, 7 must be, 8 he liked/had liked, 9 has been working, 10 is being printed, 11 not to touch